Kiki of Montparnasse

Kiki of

Montparnasse

BY FREDERICK KOHNER

STEIN AND DAY/*Publishers*/New York

In writing this memoir I have taken some liberties. While the events relating to Kiki are as true as memory will serve me, I have made some necessary changes in the description of persons other than Kiki and in the details of some events.

ALSO BY FREDERICK KOHNER

Gidget
Cher Papa
The Continental Kick

"She never had a room of her own and never was a lady at any time. But for about ten years she was as close as people get nowadays to being a Queen but that, of course, is very different from being a lady."

Ernest Hemingway about KIKI

FOR MY BROTHERS
Paul and *Walter*

CONTENTS

LIKE many a traveler I am often drawn back to the places I knew when I was very young, the battlements and barrooms of long ago. In Paris, for instance, there is a nightspot near the Metro Vavin on Montparnasse called "Le Jockey." It was "Le Jockey" forty years ago, and the name and place have miraculously survived.

It was at the Jockey that I first saw Alice Prin. She was *une bâtarde* from the Burgundy region of France who had drifted into the orbit of Montparnasse, where she became a model and everyone called her simply Kiki.

Kiki had a fine face to begin with, and she made a work of art out of it. She was warmhearted, vivacious, and ribald. A friend of prostitutes, pimps, and stray cats, she was the mistress of painters who loved her and painted her, photographers who loved her and photographed her, and writers who loved her and wrote about her.

It would never have occurred to me then to write my own story of Kiki, and it would not now, were it not for the fact that I feel the salt flood of age rising and my memory of her threatening to blur.

Kiki is long dead—and so, in a sense, is the young man I once was. We both perished together with an era in which one could order caviar for breakfast at the Café du Dôme, or buy a drawing of Modigliani's for the price of an aperitif.

An era, Hemingway wrote, is an elusive phenomenon. No one knows exactly when it starts, though everyone is pretty sure when it is over.

For me, an era started when I came to Paris to study at the Sorbonne. It was over when I left a year later.

And this is what I remember.

Kiki of Montparnasse

O N A fine, optimistic sort of a day in September, I floated up the Boulevard St. Michel in the Latin Quarter of Paris.

It was at the beginning of the Twenties and I was drunk.

Drunk with the physical beauty of a city I had just begun to discover. It was my second day in Paris. I had come there from a small town in middle Europe, with high hopes and noble purposes in my heart. I wanted to walk the very cobblestones on which students from every land had walked since the days of Charlemagne. It was my burning ambition to experience all there was to experience of what I blindly thought was the bright promise of life.

I had just turned nineteen, and like others before me, I was in search of an identity.

My father, who had lived in Paris at the turn of the century, had supplied me with the addresses of some people he had known who turned out to be long dead, a list of bistros long defunct, and a thorough briefing on the delights and dangers I might face in the foreign land—with special emphasis on the fearsome ills my flesh could become heir to. Yet with all his native wisdom and wordly knowledge, my good father had not prepared me for what I had to face within a few hours after my arrival.

I don't recall the exact time that found me drifting along the streets toward the small room I had rented, close to the Observatoire and Montparnasse. I know only that it was a lovely day, mild and autumnal, the sky dotted with pastel clouds.

So exalted did I feel, being part of that new world, already immersed in the stream of life flowing around me, that I wasn't really startled to hear a round of shots exploding on the boulevard. Only when someone grabbed me by the wrist and hurled me to the pavement did I perceive that something out of the ordinary had happened. Parisians, I learned later, had acquired great skill in this dropping-down maneuver during the last weeks of World War I, when enemy raiders would suddenly appear overhead and unleash machine guns indiscriminately on the populace. With maddening regularity, the enemy swooped down on the Boulevard St. Michel, whose venerable buildings still carried evidence of their savagery.

After I had kept my face glued to the pavement for a while and no more detonations had followed, I raised my head and looked about. People were scurrying across the street. A couple of policemen materialized and, with capes fluttering, raced toward the human conflux on the opposite side of the boulevard.

I dashed after them.

Edging my way into the circle of onlookers, I saw an elderly man sprawled out on the pavement. The light overcoat he wore was pierced by two gaping dark holes. The man was about sixty and had gray, short-cropped hair. His eyes were wide open, and he looked surprised.

There was a tense silence until someone said, *"Merde alors—il est mort comme un rat!"*

I knew enough French to agree that he was dead as a rat.

Meantime, the two *flics* had moved to stand on either side of a meek little man who wore glasses. He looked rather happily down at the punctured body. "Are you certain he is dead?" he addressed himself to all of us.

One of the *flics* released his grip, leaned down over the victim, and put an ear to his chest.

"For certain—" he pronounced. "He's dead."

A woman in the crowd screamed and fainted. The little man with the glasses gazed proudly around and then turned over to the policemen the revolver he still held in his hand.

"Then you admit it is you who shot this man?" one of the *flics* asked.

"Of course," the little man said, self-righteously.

It was the first dead man I had ever seen. And the

first murderer. I was utterly fascinated. I recall the open door of a bakery through which came the pungent smell of fresh bread. The baker came rushing out, yelling to the *flics* that help was on the way.

"You knew this man?" one of the *flics* asked the murderer.

"Not personally."

"What is his name? You know his name?"

The little man spoke the name, a foreign one.

"Why did you shoot him?"

"Why?" the little man said with heat. "You ask me *why*?"

Then he fell back on his mother tongue, which sounded to me like Yiddish. He appealed to an ever-growing circle of spectators, as if everyone would understand what he had to bring forth in his defense. And he said it well, for everyone listened without interrupting him. Unable to use his hands for emphasis (they were shackled by now), he contorted his face into furiously eloquent grimaces. Even the *flics* appeared impressed.

A police car arrived on the scene at the same time as a rickety ambulance. The killer was pushed into the car, while the dead man's body was covered with a sheet, lifted onto a stretcher, and stowed in the ambulance. The baker returned to his shop. The woman who had fainted was back on her feet. The mob dispersed. The pleasant September sun smiled upon a Latin Quarter street which reverted to normal. Nothing seemed to have changed; all was as it had been a while before.

The late evening papers carried the full story. The man shot in broad daylight had been an exiled Ukrainian general living in Paris under a *nom de guerre*. The assassin, identified as a Jewish watchmaker, had stalked his prey for years. It turned out that the harmless looking elderly gentleman with the two holes in his light overcoat had been responsible for one of the goriest pogroms in the gory history of Russian pogroms. The assassin showed no contrition. He expressed nothing but proud satisfaction for having been able to settle an account that had been long overdue.

This first encounter with violent death hounded me well into the night. I couldn't erase the surprised stare in the general's face. Sleep eluded me, and it must have been way past midnight when I finally dozed off.

I couldn't have slept long before I was awakened by a thunderous knock at the door. Then there was the voice of my landlady, Madame de la Porte.

The room I had rented on the fifth floor of an apartment house on the boul' Mich' had two doors. One led to the three rooms occupied by the landlady's family; the other was a private entrance from the stairway. This constituted a tremendous advantage over other students' rooms I had inspected, where you had to grope your way through a labyrinth of repulsive holes before you reached your rented four walls, looking out onto other walls of rotting mud brick. Female visitors to these quarters were, as a rule, prohibited. By an incredible fluke, I had found a single room with a private entrance. Madame de la Porte and her mother occupied the other three rooms of the apartment. I had so far met only my landlady and Madame *la grand'mère*—of the existence of a daughter I had been kept in ignorance.

I jumped out of bed and opened the door an inch; my landlady quickly forced it open enough to grab me by the hand.

"You must help us, Monsieur," she whispered, and before I could gather my thoughts, she had propelled me into the adjoining room.

In the far corner of it I saw a woman lying on a bed. She had long blonde hair, and as I came closer I saw beads of perspiration on her forehead. She was singing.

"This is my daughter, Alphonsine," Madame de la Porte said with dignity. "She is *enceinte*. She will have the *bebé* at any moment. You must help us, Monsieur."

Whatever resentment I felt for being roused quickly evaporated with this appeal for help. And I knew all about being *enceinte*.

Like most children of the old Austrian bourgeoisie, I had been coerced into learning another language besides my mother tongue. English or French were

de rigueur. My parents had chosen French for me,
I and was sent twice a week to Mademoiselle Marie,
the only genuine *mademoiselle* in our hometown.

The enjoyment of those hours while I walked with
Mademoiselle through the parks of my hometown has
stayed with me to this day—and to this day I won't
forget a beautiful dark-eyed gypsy girl who one day
appeared on one of the town's lovely promenades,
begging us to let her read our palms. Mademoiselle
graciously consented, and while she listened, I kept
my eyes glued to the huge belly of the gypsy girl with
the fabulous eyes. That bulge fascinated me more
than her prophetic pronouncements about the handsome stranger who—alas!—never was fated to cross
Mademoiselle Marie's path. After Mademoiselle had
paid the palmist, we continued on our promenade,
and I asked her why a young girl would be afflicted
with such an awe-inspiring protuberance.

"Elle est enceinte, mon petit ami," Mademoiselle
said sweetly. And sweetly she tried to explain it to
me, without going into clinical details as educators
nowadays would. Being *enceinte,* she told me, was the
most desirable state for a woman—which left me with
pleasant speculations on how such a mysterious condition could be achieved.

I pursued the subject further by appealing to my
older brother for more down-to-earth edification. It
was he who gave me an answer to that most fundamental of questions. So I knew about *enceinte*—but

21

that I would one night, at the age of nineteen, be called upon to help a woman in her hour of agony had not occurred to me in my most extravagant dreams.

My landlady, attired in a nightdress, dragged me to the bedside and implored me to lend her suffering daughter my strong right arm—literally! Uncomprehending, I stared at her in the flickering gaslight. *"Votre main, Monsieur!"* Madame cried and grabbed my hand, almost knocking me off balance. Only when the beautiful Alphonsine dug her fingers into the arm did I understand: I was used as a human bar on which the pregnant girl began alternately to lift herself up and then lower herself down. She accompanied these exercises with a wailing singsong, while Madame *la grand'mère* hurried back and forth, stacking up sheets, pouring hot water into a wooden bucket, and showing altogether such efficiency that an onlooker would have supposed she had done nothing all her life but minister to childbirth.

It was a scene worthy of Balzac.

For what seemed hours on end the poor girl hoisted her body up on my outstretched arm—and then relaxed. Up and down she lifted herself, up and down. Finally I asked Madame de la Porte timidly why no doctor had been called. *"Docteur—oh, non, Monsieur!"* Madame cried, as if I had suggested she call in the devil. "We cannot afford to call a doctor.

We use a *sage-femme*—but she lives far from here, in Montrouge."

There were a few other questions that occurred to me, but I was entirely too young and too dopey to ask the most obvious one: where in hell was the father of this child about to be born under such harrowing circumstances? The variety of reasons why a father might not care or bother to make an appearance didn't present themselves to me.

Because I felt that I must live up to my landlady's expectations of unquestioning assistance, I managed one of the more memorable endurance feats of my life. Right arm—left arm—bravely I stood my ground, helping Alphonsine to rid herself of her sweet burden. Her singing grew louder and more doleful as time passed. Suddenly there was a piercing scream, a wild animal howl, as if all poor women on earth had united in one voice of protest and desperation. My knees turned rubbery, and my eyes held fast to the framed print of a still life on the wall. Nothing could tempt me to look down and watch what was going on under the bed sheet. Madame *la grand'mère* was busy there with the chores normally entrusted to professional hands. After that unforgettable scream it got very still, and then we heard the soft wail of a baby's voice.

Then only did I relax—so completely that I almost doubled up on the spot.

It was a night Alphonsine would always remember, and it was certainly a night I could never forget.

Before I removed myself from the scene, Madame de la Porte insisted that I take a look at the *bebé*. I recall a wrinkled something that quaked, and then a wave of nausea rose in me and I hurried back to my own room for an uninterrupted sleep of fourteen consecutive hours.

I WOKE toward evening. In the changing light, I could see the crowns of the chestnut trees peeking through the windows. I waited till it was dark. There was no electricity in the house, so I struck a match and lit the gas lamps. Feeling well and rested, I dressed and then rushed down the stairs, out onto the boul' Mich' for another voyage of discovery.

The Latin Quarter in those days was quite different in character from the way it appears today. Not that the streets have changed in any respect, but what *happens* in the streets has undergone a distinct transformation. The streets in my day belonged to the people; even a spacious avenue like the boul' Mich' was considered public domain. The residents sat in doorways or on curbstones and crossed the street without much risk to life and limb. The boulevard was like a communal front yard. Students went about in felt slippers, and taxis stopped solicitously when children played in the middle of the thoroughfare.

Across from where I lived, a milk bar—a *crémerie*—offered a wholesome meal of bread, cheese, milk, and strawberries for a few centimes. Not far from there a restaurant run by White Russians served shashlik and kasha Guriewskaya garnished with melancholy balalaika music. When you turned the corner, you entered a crooked street with lopsided houses, all adorned with red lanterns. This street was reminiscent of similar streets in my hometown, for in the old Austro-Hungarian monarchy, whorehouses were as much a part of the scene as the double eagle or the public *pissotières*. All those landmarks of the Latin Quarter are gone by now—along with the students in their house slippers and the children playing hopscotch in the middle of the boul' Mich'.

But the Boulevard Montparnasse, which was only a short walking distance from my room, has not changed at all. There is still the Closerie de Lilas Café with its old marble and wrought-iron tables and green-shaded lamps, the Café du Dôme, the Rotonde, and the Select. And Le Jockey bar is still in existence where it first opened its doors at the beginning of the Twenties: at the corner of the Rue Chevreuse and the Boulevard Montparnasse.

What attracted me that evening as I walked down toward Metro Vavin was the neon sign which flashed the name "Le Jockey" in gaudy colors onto the pavement. Neon lights in those days were not the commonplace horror they have become since, and I was much impressed by this technical marvel.

I crossed the boulevard to take a peek behind the swinging doors.

Before I was able to decide what to do, a group of people, pushing their way into the Jockey, had swept me along.

The most remarkable thing about the Jockey was its compactness. I had never seen so many human beings boxed into such a miniscule area. There were long tables placed against the wall, the wall decorated with garish posters and crudely painted signs that read, "We've only Lost One Customer—He Died" and "If You Can't Take a Joke—Take a Walk." An industrious Negro played jazz on a piano, and over a miniature floor space, dancers seemed to have achieved a plastic unity. A thick cloud of smoke and amiability hung over the scene. There was a constant coming and going of people stepping over each other, pushing each other, and conversing in all living tongues. I found myself cemented between a *vie de Bohème* character and two girls with short hair. The one was blonde, the other dark, and they had their arms linked like lovers.

Before long I held a drink in my hand, a tall glass which I emptied at a leisurely pace. Someone took it from me and put a second one on the table. Soon there were four saucers piled up to denote the number of drinks served to me. I have a fiendish memory for odors and tastes, and the odor of those greenish concoctions and their taste come back to me whenever I close my eyes and see myself sitting in the murky limbo of the Jockey, a stowaway on Parnassus.

As a drinker I was a complete neophyte. Occasionally my father had let me take a sip from his glass of beer and—on festive occasions—wine. "Hard" liquor was an unknown commodity. Thinking back now, I'm surprised that on this first evening I didn't wind up under the table. After only one of those garish-looking liquids, I must have gotten pleasantly foggy; what happened after I had downed the second glass can only be told in broken sequences, for that is the way I remember it.

I was aware of a scrawny, undersized girl on the now empty dance floor. "Chiffonette! Chiffonette!" everyone yelled, hardly listening to her tinny voice with the heavy lisp that sounded like a scratched record as she sang.

When she had finished her songs, a man with a mane of yellow hair, a red shirt, and trousers of blue sailcloth squatted on the floor and executed some sort of a folk dance, Polish or Hungarian.

Presently there were two men. A huge one with a fierce mustache had joined the yellow-haired one, and the two kicked their legs in unison and chanted like wild tribesmen; soon everyone got into the act, yelling without the encumbrance of music.

28

Later on there was the smashing of glasses against the wall, splinters ricocheting all over the place, and a raucous chorus that yelled, "Kiki! Kiki! We want Kiki!"

Neither the years nor my state of inebriation at the time can erase my first impression of her. She wore a simple black dress; her hair was pitch dark and cut with bangs low on the forehead. She had a full mouth, white teeth, and amber-colored, green-speckled eyes with long, curved eyelashes. Her brows tilted upward to enhance fine, dauntlessly candid eyes. Her figure was on the plump side, not conforming to the then prevailing ideal of the flapper type. But it was Kiki's face that one could never forget: a face beyond childhood, yet this side of belonging to a woman.

When complete stillness had settled over the room she began to sing in a raspy voice:

"Les filles de camaret se disent toutes vierges
Les filles de camaret se disent toutes vierges
Mais quand elles sont dans mon lit
Elles preferent tenir ma vis
Qu'un cierge—qu'un cierge—qu'un cier-er-ge."

I understood only a few of the words, but Kiki came to the aid of the uninitiated. She reached for a candle and pointed it, with exaggerated daintiness, at the center of her thighs.

The audience went wild.

Without blinking an eyelid she continued:

"Mon mari s'en est allé à la pêche en Espagne.
Mon mari s'en est allé à la pêche en Espagne.
Il m'a laissé sans un sou
Mais avec mon p'tit trou
J'en gagne—j'en gagne—j'en gagn-gagn-e."

For continued clarification, she put aside the candle and simply used her index finger to point.

I understood. And I was glad for anonymity, because I felt an embarrassing awakening of desire.

She sang a third stanza, at the end of which she lifted her skirt high above her knees. The black garters against the white skin of her thighs brought on a new surge of sensuality in me.

The applause was uproarious. Now, for the first time, Kiki smiled. Then she snatched a hat from one of the customers and went around collecting money.

Reaching into my pocket to make my contribution, my heart contracted. No more money! But then I remembered that I *did* have money. It was in a yellow leather sack securely strung around my neck. In this way my father had been told by *his* father to hide his savings, and that's where I was urged to keep mine— in the same worn-down pouch my father had carried around his neck some thirty years before.

I faced a hideous problem: how could I get to my

30

money? Kiki came closer. Now she stood right in front of me. My neighbors dropped a few coins into the outstretched hat and passed it to me. I could smell Kiki's heady perfume. I unbuttoned my shirt and fumbled for the leather pouch. I tore out a bill and dropped it into the hat.

Kiki didn't move. I stared at her legs in the black silk stockings. The legs seemed rooted. I glanced up and looked into her face. She wore heavy make-up which I hadn't noticed at a distance.

Suspiciously, she gazed first at me, then at the banknote. Eventually she bent over to retrieve the bill from the hat, giving me for a moment a glimpse of her enormous breasts.

"*Américain, vous?*" she asked as if she was speaking to a child.

I shook my head.

"*Alors, tu est faux-monnayeur, toi?*" She held the banknote to the light. Understandably, she thought it might be counterfeit.

It was a fifty-franc note—enough money to sustain a student for at least a week. I kept on staring at her, too shocked at myself to ask for change. Kiki laughed, showing her magnificent white teeth. Then she lifted her skirt to offer me a close look at her lustrous thighs—and squeezed the note in between the black garters.

I had a difficult time keeping my balance on the

bench. I had the sensation that I was wearing my limbs like clothes, that they didn't really belong to my body.

Giving me a final glance of casual curiosity, Kiki moved on to the next table.

Now the blonde girl on my right was interested.

"You're not American?" she asked.

"No," I said.

"You gave her fifty francs."

"I know." I had an almost physical sense of pride and achievement. Of course no one but Americans were considered foolish enough to throw their money away. To top my brashness I called loudly for another drink.

The blonde, who was small and of fragile depravity, turned to her friend and whispered something into her ear. The music had started again, and couples dissolved onto the dance floor.

"How about?" the girl turned to me.

"Dance? Fine!" I got up.

Unsteadily I moved onto the floor. You couldn't really dance; you just held your partner in the prevailing style and weaved back and forth.

"My name's Inge," the girl said. She had a foreign accent.

I introduced myself.

"You speak French well," she said.

"So do you."

"I've been living in Paris for a year," she said. "Do you like my girl friend?"

"She looks nice," I said.

"We room together," Inge said. "We rent a studio. Not far from here. Edy is an artist."

"Who's Edy?"

"My girl friend."

She held me tightly, dainty though she was, her body hard against mine.

"Do you like Edy?"

"I guess so," I said. I was confused.

"We could have a pleasant time together," Inge said. We were very close, and what she had said puzzled me still more.

"Together?" I was hesitant in my confusion.

"The three of us," Inge went on.

Just then my eye caught Kiki, who was sitting at a table with three men. When she saw me, she suddenly got up and came over. She tapped Inge on the shoulder.

"Vingt-deux!" Kiki said sharply.

Reluctantly Inge let go of me. Kiki gave her a push.

"Merde! Tu me cours sur l'haricot!" Inge hissed at her.

Kiki shrugged off the insult. She slung her arms around me, fitting our bodies together. "She's bad, that one. You must watch out."

I looked down at Kiki's bare shoulders. Her body was so close I was breathless.

"You do not dance?" she said. "You must hold me tight, *petite grue.*"

I tried. I tried to take some steps. But the heavy perfume dizzied me.

"*Alors—toi!*" Kiki laughed as she felt my manliness. "What age have you?"

"Nineteen."

"You're a droll one," she said.

I didn't answer. I held her so close now that I could tell she wore nothing underneath her dress but those garters. No brassiere, no panties. Nothing. It became intolerable.

The music stopped.

Kiki laughed, blew me a kiss and walked away.

"Please—" I called after her. I followed her. "Can I see you again?"

"Of course," Kiki said. "Every night. Here."

"Could I invite you—for dinner?"

"No," she said, and smiled at me with her lips parted. "Not dinner. But come over to the Rotonde, six tomorrow."

"What's the Rotonde?" I asked.

She laughed.

"You are new around here, Mr. Rockefeller?"

"I've just arrived in Paris."

"Ah—*ça,*" she laughed again and told me where the Café Rotonde was—just a few blocks from the Jockey.

34

"Kiki—Kiki!" one of the men she had been sitting with called out. *"Dépêche toi, ma cocotte."*

"At the Rotonde—tomorrow," she said with a warm glance.

I didn't go back to the two lesbians. I went to the bar and paid for my drinks and left.

It was past midnight.

The air was clear and lovely. I walked farther up the boulevard, looking for the Rotonde. You couldn't possibly miss it. The Café was still crowded, the tables extending to the edge of the pavement.

I could have sat down and stayed all night and the next day till it was time to meet Kiki. I felt happy and adventurous. I will see her tomorrow, I thought. I couldn't believe my luck.

After standing around for a while on that busy street corner, I decided to go back the same way I had come. Again I passed the Closerie de Lilas and turned into the boul' Mich'. There was a little park I hadn't noticed before, with the statue of a general. I stopped to find out who it was. It was General Ney; his sword was drawn, and he looked very martial.

By two in the morning, I was finally back in my room, but I couldn't fall asleep. Outside on the boulevard, the night trains rumbled on the streetcar tracks, carrying vegetables to les Halles.

I lay awake and thought of Kiki.

NEXT morning I enrolled at the Sorbonne. I selected seven units, which was a lot. As it turned out, I hardly attended any of the courses. When I registered, my intentions were excellent, and I might have carried out my high aims had I drifted that first evening into the Negre Joyeux or the Parnasse bar instead of the Jockey.

There are crucial moments in everyone's life when the emotions one feels come ridiculously close to a cliché, but every cliché in the world has its moment of truth.

Coup de foudre! Love at first sight. From the moment I had set eyes on Kiki, I couldn't rid myself of a spell of enchantment she cast over me. The unbelievableness of her body in my arms, her beautiful breasts, the warm, inviting look, and those black garters set against the white thighs—I saw myself at the very gates of paradise, no less.

In those days I was still in the throes of my romantic stance, a stance I remember not without pleasure. I wallowed in the novels of Herman Bang and Knut Hamsun, and recited Hoelderlin and

Rilke. While most of my friends and classmates had already become habitues of our local whorehouses, and had succeeded in seducing some of the town's virgins, I still lived in a world of unnamed passion and female veneration. The complete possession of a woman's body was still a far-off dream. Now that I had cut the family ties, I was sure the dream was about to become reality. For the first time I was filled with a rapturous sense of complete freedom.

I would meet Kiki that evening. How would I behave? What clever words would I say? How could I put myself in a flattering light? Would I succeed in inviting her to my room on that first rendezvous? I felt feverishly restless, sick with impatience.

Long before the appointed hour, I was on my way to the Rotonde. As I walked along the boulevard, it was as if a curtain were being lifted for me—a new life spread out its great boundless vista.

At this early hour the café was already overcrowded, spilling its complement of customers onto the sidewalk.

I found a table, ordered a coffee, and enjoyed everything around me. There was a peculiar smell that emanated from the coffeehouse terraces on Montparnasse, and I only have to close my eyes to bring it all back to me: the rich mixture of cigarette smoke, garlic, hot chocolate, *fine à l'eau,* burned almonds, hot chestnuts, and—all pervading—the strong scent of a perfume that had just become the rage of

37

Paris: l'Heure Bleue, and it was l'Heure Bleue that had clung to Kiki the first evening I met her.

Every time I got a whiff of the scent I felt the beating of my heart. It was past six. The waiter approached and flicked his napkin over the table. I ordered another coffee. A girl stopped by, selling one of the avant-garde magazines which sprouted in those days on Montparnasse. She was not unattractive, but her nails were dirty. Her hair was black as a crow's wing, and it cut diagonally across her cheek. I told her that I was not interested.

"You don't have to be interested," she said frankly. "But I need the money. Be a nice fellow and buy one."

I bought a copy.

"I knew you were a nice fellow," she said, and kept the change. "Will you buy me a drink?"

It was as easy as that to make contact with girls.

"I am waiting for someone," I said.

"Everyone here is waiting for someone," she said. Now I noticed that she had hawk's eyes, and a thin mouth. She was pretty in a mean way, just as Kiki was beautiful in a generous way.

"Maybe some other time," she said, disinterested, and went on.

The tables around me mushroomed. I wondered who these people were who seemed to have no worry in the world and who drifted from one coffeehouse to the next—from the Rotonde to the Select, and across the boulevard to the Dôme. A group of Americans marched by and yelled: *"Vive la France et les pommes frites!"* And a chorus of Frenchmen came back with "Long live America and central heating!"

The waiter set the coffee on the table and stacked the saucers with the prices on them. When I looked up, I saw Inge and Edy. I had left the previous evening without saying goodbye, and now I felt awkward. They immediately moved in on me. As they drew chairs up at my table I protested: "I'm waiting for someone."

"Oh, that's all right with us. We don't mind, do we, Edy?"

"No, we don't," said Edy.

Inge sat down and attached her leg to mine.

"You disappeared very suddenly last night," she said.

"I was tired."

"I don't think you were so tired," Inge said flatly. "I think it was that *putain*."

"*Putain*?"

"Whore," she said.

"You are gross."

"And you're naive. We know Kiki, don't we, Edy?"

Edy nodded.

"That money you carry under your shirt won't last long with that *putain*," Inge went on, savoring the word.

She disturbed me, but at the same time the word

39

putain excited me. The chivalrous thing, I thought, was to get up and leave. I called for the waiter.

"We don't want to chase you away," said Inge and pressed her flank more tightly to mine. "If your friend doesn't show up, we can have dinner together. You can take us to the 'Toulouse' up the boulevard. It's not too expensive, and afterwards we'll show you our studio, won't we, Edy?"

"If we have to," Edy shrugged.

"Don't listen to her," Inge said, laughing. "She's just jealous. But I'll give you a good time. Not like Kiki—she'll only give you the *douleur*."

"And maybe a look at her big tits—if you pay her," Edy said.

Shocked, I drew back from her.

"I think you're vile," I said, ready to leave.

"She is telling the truth," Inge said. "Only a year ago anyone could have had a look at Kiki's titties for three francs—behind the Gare Montparnasse. And probably for ten francs you could have humped her. Now she has a *régulier*—so the price has gone up."

I would have liked to find out more, but at the same time I felt resentful. I didn't want to be a party to this. I got up and walked away from the two of them as I had walked away the previous evening— wordless. I planted myself at the corner of the Rotonde, facing Metro Vavin, watching the unending stream of people and listening to the cries of itinerant vendors of sugared fruit and cheap carpets. Slowly the lights on the boulevard and in the coffeehouses were turned on. The evening descended, warm and quick. In no time it was night. She would not come; I was certain of it now. I had been stood up. I felt lonely and defeated.

I tried to invent excuses for Kiki. Maybe she had fallen sick and couldn't reach me. Maybe, because of my bookish French, I had misunderstood her. I walked up the north side of the Boulevard Montparnasse and stopped in front of the Jockey. The neon lights weren't on yet. I walked slowly past the bar, but then decided to turn around and take a look in the nightclub.

The door stood slightly ajar, and I went in.

The leftover smell of cigarettes and beer still permeated the place. Chairs rested, bottoms down, on the tables around the wall. There was only one naked light bulb burning. All the warmth of the Jockey had been drained.

A man sat behind the bar. He was so engrossed in what he was doing that he hadn't noticed me. As I approached him, I recognized the bartender. I had caught a glimpse of him the preceding evening and had been intrigued because he was such a tall man and because he had dark, copper-colored skin. I had never seen anyone with coppery skin.

"Good evening," I said.

The bartender looked up.

"Not open yet," he said courteously and returned to the book he was reading. It was Plato's *Republic*.

"When do you open?"

"Around ten."

"Is it Plato—in the original?" I asked.

"No," he said. "French translation."

"I've read Plato in Greek!"

Now he looked up with an assessing squint. At close range his face was even more swarthy and leathery than I had remembered. He had a large, rather hooked nose. I couldn't even guess at his age.

"You read Plato in Greek?" he said.

"I had to read Greek in school," I told him.

"It must be wonderful to read Plato in Greek," he said in a gentle voice, and read aloud a passage from the book. " 'He who is of a calm and happy nature will hardly feel the pressure of age, but to him who is of an opposite disposition, youth and age are equally a burden.' " He looked up at me: "Say that in Greek for me."

"I wish I could—" I faltered, feeling a cheat.

He closed the book and put it on a shelf behind the bar. Then he got up—or better, he rose, because his movements were very slow and dignified—and reached out for a white bar jacket and slipped it on.

"Now we are open for business," he said. "What will you have?"

I had no intention of settling down, but the man fascinated me, and I swung onto a bar stool and ordered a *demi-blonde*. He reached for a bottle and poured the beer into a glass. Behind the bar hung several photos of celebrities; one showed Kiki in a dancing pose.

"Is that Kiki?" I asked and pointed to the photo.

"Yes—that is Kiki," he said, and gave me another measuring look from slanted eyes.

"Will she sing tonight?"

"One never knows."

"She sang last night."

"Yes, she did."

"I was here."

"I know it," he said. "You danced with her."

I was surprised. "How come you recognized me?"

"I make it a point to notice everyone who dances with Kiki," he answered.

Was he the *régulier* those lesbians had mentioned, I wondered?

"May I ask you something?" I started carefully.

He nodded.

"What's a *régulier*?"

"What it says—a *régulier*. A steady."

"I met some girls up at the Rotonde who talked about Kiki. They said she has a *régulier*."

"She has."

"Are—are you her *régulier*?"

The dark man blinked. But the question didn't embarrass him; on the contrary, he seemed to be vaguely amused to have had it asked.

"No," he said, "I'm an old friend of Kiki's. A buddy, a *copain,* you might say."

His features wore as much expression as the bottle of beer.

Who was this mysterious man? He didn't look a bit like a bartender but rather—well, as I imagined Winnetou had looked, Winnetou, the redskin hero of Wild West books I had devoured in my childhood.

"May I ask you one more question?" I said.

"Go ahead."

"Are you an American?"

I felt too timid to ask if he was an Indian.

"Sure. American. American Indian. Ever heard of the Cherokees?"

"The Indian tribe?"

"One hundred percent Cherokee. At home I'm a chief. Chief Gitche Manitou."

I was thrilled to have made the acquaintance of an Indian chieftain. If I only could entice him to go on talking, I thought, and get him to tell me about himself and Kiki. If only no one would enter the bar and interfere. I ordered another demi-blonde, and as he poured it I told him how honored I was to meet a real live Indian chief and that I was dying to know how he had made the changeover from the Wild West to Montparnasse.

"A lot of people around know the story," Gitche Manitou said, "but by repetition it gets all balled up. It's a simple story, really. I traveled with a Wild West Show, and we played the Cirque d'Hiver. One night a man came to see it and offered me a job. He told me he had just opened a café and needed some kind of a stunt to stimulate business. First I didn't quite understand. I could do a number of wild things on a horse—but in a café? I asked him, 'What would I have to do?' Nothing, he said. You will just sit in my café and eat and drink. Just eat and drink and sit? That's all, he said. I told him I would like to think about it. Next day I went up to Montparnasse and looked at the place. Café du Dôme—down at the next corner."

"I've seen it," I said. It was the café just across from the Rotonde, where I had waited for Kiki.

"Well, that's the place where I sat—for two years. Sat there in Indian gear and stimulated business."

"How did you do that?" I asked, spellbound.

"Just sitting there," he continued. "Most people had never seen an Indian. So they came to the Dôme. They wanted to sit at my table. They wanted to talk about Indians, about America. Then there were painters. They came to paint me. That's how Chambon—he's the man who runs the Dôme—attracted artists. That's how he made business. That's how the café became a *succès fou*."

There was about him an air of sleepy poise.

"And you just sat there, for two years—doing *nothing*?" I said incredulously.

For the first time his face came awake.

"If you call learning how to read and to write doing nothing, then I did nothing. If you call being able to understand great writers nothing, I did nothing. And if you call getting to know all the bums and bad women of Montparnasse nothing, then I did nothing."

"And how come you now work in this nightclub?"

"I got bored at the Dôme," he answered dispassionately. "Also I could not stand the sight of the riffraff on Montparnasse any longer. I wanted to go back to Oklahoma."

There was a note of sorrow and regret in his voice.

"But you stayed on—and right on Montparnasse?"

"It was because of Kiki."

"Kiki?"

"Yes, Kiki—but that's another story."

He clammed up. I must have hit a raw nerve in him. He came from behind the bar and began setting up the chairs in the stark light of the single bulb. As I watched him, I wondered what his relationship to Kiki was. I thought about the passage of Plato he had read and wondered whether he had referred to himself as one who was not of a calm and happy nature and to whom age is a burden. Untutored and inexperienced as I was, I sensed a deep sorrow and loneliness in the Indian chieftain. I thought I could be his

46

friend, but I also wanted, in a self-serving way, to pump him about Kiki.

Just as I was about to try to get more information out of him, a heavy-set man in well-worn clothes and an artist's flapping hat entered the bar.

"Gitche?" he roared.

" *'Soir, monsieur.*" The Indian's voice came from the dark side of the room.

"An absinthe, if you please!"

The Indian switched off the single bulb and turned on the house lights; another evening at the Jockey had begun.

I LEFT the Jockey and went home and tried to put her out of my mind. I tried to sleep but couldn't. I tried to write a letter to my family but couldn't. Nothing seemed to help my restlessness. I went out into the street again and headed toward Montparnasse.

It was eleven by the time I stood in front of the neon sign. The place was jam-packed. I managed to squeeze myself into the bar but hardly found room to stand. I caught Chief Manitou's eye, and my own eyes asked him about Kiki. He responded with a noncommittal shrug.

Eventually the lights dimmed and Chiffonette sang some sailor ditties in her small, shivering voice. Since she was the least attractive of the girls who appeared at the Jockey, she was always the one to start out the evening.

After Chiffonette came Marcelle, a very pretty dark-haired girl whose face had an unused, virginal quality. Marcelle gave a clever imitation of an American film star who was famous for wiggling her behind. She undulated her posterior so provocatively that the performance drew whistles and catcalls and rowdy remarks from the customers. Her act was followed by a saxophone number rendered by Ben, the Negro piano player.

I hung around until three in the morning, hoping for Kiki to arrive, and then went dejectedly home.

I was back the next evening.

It was early and I found a chair. Taking courage, I walked over to Gitche Manitou and asked whether Kiki would show up. He gave me the same cryptic reply: "One never knows."

I ordered *fine à l'eau* and instead of nursing the drink, like a real habitué, I drank it as though it were water. The effect was immediate: the evening swam. Time slipped away. I heard the by-now familiar songs of Chiffonette and Marcelle, but only their melodies registered, no words at all. Faces left and new ones appeared.

Suddenly my heart gave a great, swift bound of happiness. Kiki was in the room, standing under the spotlight. She was beautiful, oh, was she beautiful! She sang a then-popular song, *"Nini, peau de chien."* Again she wore her black dress, again she lifted her skirt, again the audience roared, again she made the rounds with a borrowed hat. She looked at me with a curious, half-mocking intentness. Yet while she looked at me, I had the feeling she didn't recognize me. Was it possible? *"Bonsoir,* Kiki!" I stammered. A frost came over her eyes. She shrugged and moved on.

Stunned by her behavior, I had not given her anything. Now I reached into my pocket and took out
some money and yelled, "Kiki, Kiki—" but she didn't
return. She finished her rounds, lifted a couple of
fingers to her mouth and blew a kiss.

Moved by anger and starved, sorrowful passion, I
got up and followed her. Impossible that she had not
recognized me. She had turned the contents of the hat
over to Ben the piano player (later on I learned that
he divided the spoils in equal parts among all the
performers) and had placed herself on the lap of a
man at one of the tables near the piano. He was a
good-looking man with deep-set eyes and long sideburns, the one who had been her companion before.
When I stood before her, I first had to overcome a
humiliating struggle for breath. Kiki looked at me
coolly, appraisingly. Again I was overwhelmed by her
ravenous sexuality. My anger unbottled itself at her:
"We had a rendezvous!" I said. "Why didn't you
come?"

She stared at me uncomprehendingly, and then she
broke into a gale of laughter. *"Tu est fou, toi!"* she
cried. "A rendezvous? I have never seen you in my
life, *mon chou.*"

"Two nights ago," I persisted. "I danced with
you."

"Did I dance with him?" she turned to her escort.

"You were ginny, *ma cocotte,*" the man said

pleasantly. *"Cela va sans dire.* You danced with everybody."

"Not with him." She was quite positive. She stared at me with such bland innocence that I wondered if I had really gone mad and had imagined everything. I felt a wave of the most abject shame. Music started and couples paired on the floor. I was jostled and pushed as I stumbled back to my table.

It was a ridiculous puzzle. Was it beneath her to admit in the presence of her *régulier* that she had made a date with a young punk? Had I acted foolishly and irrationally?

Whatever it was that had moved her to behave the way she had, it dispirited and injured me. I watched her on the floor, dancing—molded to her partner as if in the act of love. A sultry, passionate rebellion stirred me. I called the waiter for another *fine à l'eau.* From then on I remember only phantoms surging in a blurry haze, knees slightly crooked, haunches taut, ankles swimming. Between dances and between saucers piling up in front of me there was a wild diaphony of piano and saxophone, and then things blotted out.

* * *

It was halfway through the morning, and I felt a weight on me. I opened my eyes and saw a large animal sitting on my chest. I yelled.

The animal vanished.

The pillow beneath my head was wet. A mild sun filtered through the windows.

The blood pounded inside my head, and I was so thirsty I longed for a gallon of water, just as a starter. I sat up. It was a room I had never seen before. On the window sill was that huge animal, a black cat, its eyes glaring at me in alert hostility. Then I heard a strange noise, not from the cat. It came from some other direction of the room. I stood up. I was fully dressed.

The noise came from the corner of the room, where someone was lying in bed, snoring. I stumbled over and gazed at the sleeping person.

It was Gitche Manitou. In his sleep he looked very old.

How had I come here? I tried to collect my thoughts. What time was it? Daytime, anyway: the sun was shining. What had happened? I noticed a wash basin with a mirror fixed above it. Like a thief I tiptoed over and gazed uneasily at my reflection: the long, unfashionable hair, the long neck, the high forehead, the glasses. It wasn't a pleasant image that gazed back from the mirror, but at least I had the sense of catching up with myself. It was me all right, but God! how awful I looked!

I turned on the faucet of the wash basin and let water run over my face and hair. Then I bent still lower and let the cold water pour into my mouth.

There were two clean towels hanging from a rack. I took one and dried myself.

Carefully, so as not to wake my host, I crossed over to the single window and looked out. There wasn't much to see. We were two floors up; the house across the street, its windows shuttered, had flaky, soot-gray stone walls. The street below was narrow and carried little traffic.

I turned back to inspect the room. There was a shelf with books, above it a framed picture. I stepped closer and recognized Kiki. It was a delicate painting, signed by a Japanese artist. The book titles were mostly French—Balzac, Verlaine, Montaigne—but I saw also a collection of Walt Whitman poetry and a copy of the Bible. In another corner stood a stove. It was a clean but melancholy room.

Once more I stepped close to the sleeping Indian. Against the white of the pillows the copper darkness of his face was startling. Otherwise it seemed tranquil, like water under a bridge. Then, just as I began to turn and walk away, he opened his eyes.

Under his quiet gaze I felt depraved and unclean.

"Good morning," I said guiltily.

The cat leaped on his bed and began meowing. He stroked her gently.

"*Tais toi*, Mouchette," he said.

"Please tell me what happened," I said, fighting my embarrassment. "How did I get here?"

"Too much firewater," he said and sat up. "How do you feel?"

"Not too bad," I said, telling the truth.

"That's no good," said Gitche Manitou. He reached for a dark-brown terrycloth robe and got up.

"Why is it no good?"

"If you get drunk for the first time and don't feel bad afterward, you go on drinking."

"No, I won't," I protested.

The Indian chieftain's eyebrows rose in prodigious arches.

"It will be the first and last time—I promise."

"Okay," he said. "I believe you."

"How did I get up here?" I asked. "I can't remember a thing."

"We carried you," Gitche Manitou said.

"We?"

"Ben helped."

"The piano player?"

"We're friends," said Gitche Manitou.

"I'm terribly grateful," I said. "Believe me, this has never happened to me before. Never."

"I believe all that," he said. "I think I know what happened last night." From the look on his face and the tone of his voice, I was sure that he did know. He must have a great insight into human beings, I thought.

"Sit down," Gitche Manitou said. "I'll make you

54

some coffee." He poured water into a coffeepot and turned on the gas on the stove.

"I don't know how to thank you," I said lamely.

"Never mind," he said. "A man can get mixed up in all sorts of things. We'll have coffee and then you'll feel fine. Coffee is good for you. Puts a man on a horse."

I thanked him and sat down. While we waited for the water to boil, the Indian said, "Tell me about yourself. Where do you come from? What's your name?"

I told him. I told him about my family and my background, and why I had come to Paris, and how everything had affected me during the first days in the big city.

After listening impassively to my narrative, he said, "I thought you were a clean boy. That's why I didn't call the *flics* but lugged you up." And then, guessing at what I had omitted, he said, "I figured it was Kiki who got you into getting drunk. Did I figure it right?"

I nodded.

"It's not the first time a man's gotten drunk on account of Kiki," he said pensively. "It's not her fault, mind you. She just affects men that way."

I was touched by his friendly, earnest concern and glad I could talk about Kiki.

"When I danced with her the first evening, she

made a rendezvous with me. But she didn't show up.
And last night she pretended she had never seen me.
It made me so furious I got drunk."

His eyes narrowed.

"She does it all the time. To most people. Not to
her friends, not to her *régulier*."

"Is the man with the sideburns her *régulier*?"

"Yes, he's the one."

"Who is he?"

"A painter."

"Does she live with him?"

He nodded.

"And before that?"

"Before that there was another painter."

"Has she ever lived with you?"

"Yes, she lived here—a short time. Slept on that
couch where you were sleeping."

He shuffled over to the stove. The water was
boiling now, and the coffee started to percolate.
Gitche Manitou put everything on a tray, cups,
saucers and sugar, and laid it on the table—very
neatly.

"How old do you think I am?" he asked me
unexpectedly.

"Oh, around fifty," I said, figuring him about fifty-
five.

"I'm shy one month of sixty-five," he said.

"I can't believe it."

"I've always lived a clean life," he said. "Never touch spirits. Never been married. I could have stayed with the circus."

"Can't you go back to it?"

"Too old," Gitche Manitou said. "I meant to go back to Oklahoma. But now I won't. I guess I'll stay here and read Plato and die in this room."

He said it without emotion and poured the coffee. Now I realized that he was an old man. In his faded bathrobe, he finally seemed truly old.

"But you told me the other night that you stayed in Montparnasse because of Kiki," I said, hoping I could loosen his tongue.

"She got under your skin, did she?"

"I guess so," I answered uneasily, having never before heard the expression.

He gave me one of those strange looks I would get used to, a mixture of resignation and compassion.

"Okay," he said finally. "I'll tell you what I know about her."

He began the story.

IT WAS January, said Gitche Manitou, and it got dark early. I sat in the Dôme, at my usual table close to the window. I sat with Wambly Bald. He was an easy-going man who wrote about *la vie de Bohème* for an American newspaper; he was out to get his story for the column. Wambly always needed new stories for his paper, and sometime he got one from me. But not this afternoon. I was thinking black thoughts. I felt sick, sitting there with my Indian trappings, doing nothing.

Paris is fine in the spring and summer, but in winter the city is like an old woman who shows her age. I had good food and a warm room and I had some money, but I felt sick inside. Tourists stayed away in winter, and the café was filled with the lowest types—bums and sots and bad women. I knew them all and I despised them. I only held out because of the money I put into the bank. When I had enough money put away, I thought, I would go back to my country.

Then I saw this girl staring at me through the window. She had a pretty face and a smooth skin and her eyes were big. A *poule* looking for her evening meal, I thought. Then I noticed something strange. She wore no shoes. It had snowed and there was slush in the streets, and she had bare feet. Look at her, I said to Wambly, she has no shoes. Wambly looked up. She smiled at him. Bring her in, I said. Wambly thought it was a fine idea.

I watched through the window. Wambly talked to her, and they were both laughing. I wondered what she had to laugh about with her frozen feet. Then she followed him inside.

Everyone in the place looked at her. In her rags and bare feet she walked like a princess. First thing she asked was, are you a real Indian? It was the usual question. Sure, I told her, I'm an Indian. Marvelous, she said. She had never seen an Indian, except in the movies.

Her teeth were chattering. Aren't you hungry? I asked her. Plenty, she said, but first I must drink.

She snapped her fingers for Auguste and ordered a Pernod. Then she started talking. She talked prodigously, and I didn't understand too much. I asked Wambly. It's argot, he told me, Burgundese. Wambly understood her and was all ears. The way she talked, the way he listened, I knew he had a good story. After a while he said, Mind if I take some notes? Why notes? I might write a piece about you. Do I get paid? No, but everyone will read about you. She was not impressed. You pay me ten francs and I talk, she said.

Wambly agreed to pay her ten francs. Okay, he said now tell me your name. It's Alice Prin, she answered, but everyone calls me Kiki. Just write Kiki, she said, maybe my mother will read about it, and her name is Prin, and I don't want her to find me. Where is your mother? Here in Paris, she said, but I never see her. And who is your father? A good question. She laughed.

Then she went on telling Wambly how she got to Paris from Burgundy, how she had never had any schooling, had worked in a factory, on the flower market in the rue Mouffetard, for a baker, for a pimp.

You worked for a pimp? Wambly perked up. Yes, she said, but not the way you think. I kept house for him and his *poule*. I slept in the same room with them, but he never touched me. I don't believe it, Wambly said. His *poule* would have killed me, Kiki said. The *poule* worked for him, and when she came home, they went to bed and made love. I watched them, it was a good education. And he didn't seduce you? Wambly asked. *Merde, non,* Kiki said. I had my own little business. And what was your business? I got two francs for showing my bosom, she said proudly. Sometimes I got five francs. I have a terrific bosom.

I looked at her bosom. It was firm and resilient, and she wore no brassiere. When she saw me looking, she said, You're a nice *grue*. I'll show them to you for nothing.

60

Wambly asked some more questions, and when he had enough to write about, he paid her ten francs and left.

I was alone with her, and she looked at me and was very quiet, and I had a new feeling inside me, a feeling I had thought I had lost forever.

Where do you live? I asked her.

Not far from here, she answered, behind the Gare Montparnasse.

You have a room?

Just a sandbag.

You sleep on a sandbag?

On a sandbag in a shed.

Isn't it cold?

Yes. And after a pause she said, Indians sleep under the stars. They must be cold too.

Yes, I told her, they're cold.

Then she asked me what I was doing at the Dôme with my Indian gear and why I was not living with other Indians. I told her why.

You are being paid for the same thing I am being paid for, she said.

I had to admit she was right.

But you made a face when I said I am taking money for showing my bosom.

There is a difference, I told her.

No, she said, there is no difference. And then she asked, Do Indians believe in God?

I told her they do.

But God has taken their country away from them.

They still believe in God.

When I was a child, I believed in God, she said. But one day I had to go to a hospital. I had some misery with my heart and went to the Cochin hospital. The nuns made me take a bath, and I had to put on a nightshirt. My heart was burning, and they said, There you see what you get for being a bad girl. They thought I was taking cocaine. I was up all night. My heart jumped like crazy, and I almost died. It was only fright. All you could hear was moans and death rattles. There was an old woman in the next bed; she was over a hundred years old, and all night she was whining, The pot, for the mercy of the Lord. But no one came. In the morning the nuns found her bed wet. One shouted, Aren't you ashamed of yourself, doing a thing like this at your age?

That's when I said to myself the hell with God!

It was dark by now and the bright lights in the café were turned on. She had had three Pernods and a couple of sandwiches, and now she got up and thanked me.

Where are you going? I asked her.

Nowhere.

Wouldn't you like to have a place to go to?

I have my sandbag.

Wouldn't you rather sleep in a bed?

She looked at me with her big eyes, and said, You've got a bed for me?

In my room, I said.

How old are you?

I told her. I also told her she had nothing to worry about.

Tant pis, she answered, I hoped you would teach me. My mother told me there is nothing like being seduced by an old man when it comes to losing your virginity painlessly.

I'm too old, I told her. An Indian, when he is fifty, he is old. I am over sixty.

I once met a man who was fifty, Kiki said. He made quite a hit with me. He lived in Melimontant. He had worked in a circus as a clown and his wife was on a tour, so he took me home. He made me take off my clothes and gave me one of his wife's nightgowns. I went to bed with him, hoping I would learn all about love. He lay down beside me and did many nice things, but in the morning I was still a virgin.

I worked for years in a circus, I told her.

Circus people are swell, she said. You seem to be a nice *grue,* and I'll come and live with you—but only if I can bring Mouchette along.

Who's Mouchette? I asked her.

A cat, she said. I found it a few days ago. Black and all covered with fleas. I stole a bottle of milk and fed it with an eyedropper. It lives with me in the shed.

She went to get Mouchette, and she moved in with me, and it was the best time of my life. It was winter, but my black thoughts went away and I was happy.

She made the bed for me and mopped the room and washed and cleaned and sometimes cooked meals. I never took advantage of her and disgraced myself. You often hear of old men disgracing themselves when they feel the burden. I felt the burden, but I never put my thoughts into action. You can love someone without it being that way. You keep your feelings locked inside you.

Of course I knew it would not last. One night she didn't come home, and the next day she asked me whether I would keep the cat. She had found a man who loved her, a painter. She had modeled for him, and he had asked her to live with him.

That was three years ago.

Sometimes, Gitche Manitou concluded, she comes to visit here. I like to think she wants to see me, but I know it's because of Mouchette.

Here, have another cup of coffee.

WHAT Gitche Manitou had told me, as well as the discoveries I made on my own, only increased the desire Kiki had awakened in me. I felt attracted toward her as I had never felt attracted toward anyone.

She was, of course, nothing like the women I had dreamed of, those goddesses I had conceived and worshipped. We seemed to have not a taste in common. Our characters and dispositions were wholly different. Besides being foreign, she was something unique, a totally new image.

The girls I had known were the girls of my hometown, familiar from childhood. I had skated, skiied, danced, and petted with them. These girls lived in well-lighted houses with rich, comfortable rooms; they wore proper clothes, went to proper schools, and had proper manners. They were "nice" girls who stayed virgins until, eventually, you married them.

There were also the girls who were less nice—the ones who had a "reputation." They were not socially acceptable. They offered sex, but with it the possibility of pregnancy, which meant disaster.

Then of course there were the whores.

Considering the small size of our town, whorehouses were numerous. An aura of mystery, sin, and pleasure surrounded them. But temptation vanished in the cold light of my father's detailed recital of the horrible consequences a visit to the red light district would produce. I was shown stark explicit photographs of V.D. cases by our alerted family doctor. They nauseated me. Frightened and disenchanted, I shrank from the idea of visiting a brothel.

Those were the three worlds of women that I knew about. Three doors—all closed to me. I felt cursed with what seemed to be everlasting celibacy.

Kiki gave promise of lifting the curse.

Her prestige and success in Montparnasse circles seemed to me closely related to bourgeois respectability. Prestige and success also — curiously — gave her a warrant of good health. Why these two should have been allied I can't say, but there it was.

All the bottled-up sensuality of adolescence reacted to her great hips, the soft power of her legs, her voluptuous mouth, her seductive eyes. Here was sex without hypocrisies and inhibitions, glorified openly by a beautiful woman.

I thought of her unceasingly and haunted the places she frequented, the bars and cafés and bistros of Montparnasse. I often saw her at the Jockey, and I devised all sorts of schemes to contrive a face-to-face confrontation, but she never quite seemed to see me. Sometimes I followed her at night when she left the Jockey with her painter friend. Mostly they attended studio parties to which I had no entrée. And so I patrolled the streets, just hoping for a glimpse of her. Even my dreams centered around her.

I tried to argue away my obsession by telling myself over and over again that she was in all likelihood nothing but a prostitute, that if only I had enough money to pay, she would satisfy my passion as she must have satisfied others before me. But in not having access to money, except for the modest allowance I received from home, and thus not being able to possess her, I was possessed by her.

Neglecting my studies, I made Kiki my study. I ransacked her past, hoping that by discovering the different components of her earlier years, I would somehow make her completely my own, if only in an imaginary fashion. I had embarked on a most difficult investigation, for I had to fill in the years that had elapsed since she had left Gitche Manitou. And in those three years she had had a multitude of *réguliers* and had slept in a multitude of beds. Some of her *réguliers* had lasted weeks, some just days. But they all had one thing in common.

They were all artists.

Artists had discovered Kiki. They liked to use her as a model, not only because of her vivid beauty and seductiveness, but because Kiki had made an art of modeling. Her face could express every shading of mood, her body could adapt itself to the most provocative of postures. Painters whose names were known the world over—Utrillo, Foujita, Kisling—used her as a model. She posed for them, and she entertained them with gay and bizarre stories. If she liked the artist well enough, she stayed at his studio, cooked his meals, slept in his bed. When she left, there were never any scenes. No passionate dramas were enacted. No one seemed to have suffered from the parting, because both she and her friends knew that the commitment was only temporary. Everyone respected the freedom and independence which were fundamentally Kiki's most distinctive characteristics.

The fanaticism with which I tried to immerse myself in her personality, the singlemindedness with which I pursued my research, drove me eventually to the studio of the painter she was then living with, in the Rue Vaugirard.

The somber houses of that street faced the lovely Jardin du Luxembourg. It was the beginning of October, and the garden had exploded in a riotous display of autumn colors: shrubs with garnet leaves, dahlias, and asters in beautiful designs. I recall especially the wildly. sprouting chrysanthemums of that fall, because it was behind a chrysanthemum bush that I took up my position, determined to besiege 92 Rue Vaugirard.

68

The studio of Kiki's friend was situated on the top floor of the building. Other tenants of the house belonged to the typical French bourgeoisie: fading ladies with parched faces; small officials who left the house at a fixed time and returned at the stroke of six; housewives who took their dogs for an outing in the early afternoons; and the concierge, who set up her folding chair in front of the massive house door, watching the passersby. The most conspicuous resident of number 92 Rue Vaugirard was a jolly bon vivant with white hair and the ribbon of the Legion D'Honneur in his lapel. Every afternoon he left the house at four, entered the Luxembourg through a side gate, and took his constitutional for precisely one hour, returning home as the stroke of five sounded from nearby Saint Sulpice. He was greeted with great deference by the concierge, the newspaper vendor at the corner, and by practically everyone whose path he happened to cross.

Occasionally the iron, fenced-in balcony on the second floor offered a fine spectacle: a sprightly, not unattractive female tenant appeared with a wooden washtub, submerged into it her speckled terrier, and gave it a thorough scrubbing. The dog howled in protest for all to hear. The bath over, she wrapped the mutt in a towel and, having dried it, lifted it up proudly to show it off to her neighbors who had (as if responding to a pre-arranged curtain call) appeared on their respective balconies to watch the performance. It was the kind of public entertainment dear to the Paris bourgeoisie, the casual kind that was so much a part of French community life.

The only inhabitants of this area whose schedule did not follow a set pattern were the painter and Kiki. They left and arrived at odd times, but always together. Whenever I saw them emerging from the building, my heart began pounding against my chest. I would abandon my post behind the flower bushes and follow them at a distance, straining my eyes, staring miserably at their intertwined arms, until they disappeared into the Metro or a taxicab.

Driven by some obsessive urge, I would return to my observation post and the nothing-but-masochistic pleasure I seemed to derive from their openly displayed caresses. Why did I do it? What did I expect to gain? Recalling those incredibly wasted hours, it seems now that what I was waiting for was a waning in their amorous relationship, but, as passionately as I prayed for it, I saw no sign of a change.

Finally it was Gitche, the Indian chieftain, who provided me with a clue to an approach.

Since the night I had slept in his room and he had told me what he knew of Kiki, we had become friends.

I learned that his seeming indifference and stoicism were the protective coloring of a temperament whose inmost recesses held a deep reservoir of emotion. He suffered over the loss of Kiki. "Loss" may be an inaccurate description of his suffering, for he had never possessed her. I sensed the agony of his spirit, which could find no outward expression. I was never able to talk to him about my feeling for Kiki, but he felt it instinctively, and our mutual longing for her was the strongest bond between us. He always had a bar stool hidden, so as to make room for me when the Jockey was bursting at the seams. I sat for hours, nursing a single drink, waiting for a moment when Kiki would make her brief appearance. But I would often drop in on him at home in the early afternoon. Our talks then usually centered around books, and I was happy to try to repay his many kindnesses by advising him on reading matters. I had at that time tried my hand at a couple of short stories, and when I mentioned it, he asked me to read them to him. Since few authors, particularly unpublished ones, can resist an invitation to read aloud, I grabbed this chance to use my friend Manitou as a sounding board.

"Good stories," he said after listening. I was thrilled; after all, this judgment came from a well-read man. I took his comment for approval and encouragement.

Secretly I hoped Kiki would come to Gitche's room to pay one of her occasional visits to Mouchette. Though I disliked cats, I cultivated Mouchette, who learned to cuddle up to me the moment I entered the chieftain's room.

It was from Gitche Manitou that I learned about a

change in Kiki's life: she had become a painter. Under the guidance of her present *régulier,* she had made some tentative experiments in black-and-white, and they had proved so charming that she was encouraged to execute a whole series of them. In those days an artist, if he had the right connections, was quickly touted, exhibited—and bought. The Indian had seen none of these paintings, but he knew an exhibit was in the making.

Eventually I decided to make a legitimate call on Kiki with the intention of buying one of her drawings before they went on exhibit. I had recently received a twenty-dollar check from my brother, who was finding his livelihood in America. Twenty dollars, converted into the then inflated French franc, was an astronomical amount.

It was a gray October afternoon, precisely at four, when I abandoned my sentinel post and executed my plan.

The bon vivant had just left the house, but he was not alone: Kiki's paramour came out with him. They were engaged in a lively conversation and walked together to the corner. There they shook hands—the bon vivant proceeding on his usual route, Kiki's friend stepping into a cab.

This was the moment to act. I ran across the street and entered the house. I felt for the still uncashed twenty-dollar check in my pocket and raced up the dark staircase, my heart thumping madly.

When I stood in front of the studio door, my muscles seemed to have lost contact with their nerve center. I waited for a few minutes, trying to calm the tumult inside me. The house was silent. My fingers still held the only tangible security I had, the twenty-dollar check.

Eventually I summoned the strength to knock at the door. I waited. No one answered. Somehow I felt relieved. Maybe she isn't home, I thought. Maybe she left before I took up my spying post. Yet I rapped once more on the door.

Then I heard a noise.

I stood rigid.

The door opened.

The girl in the dim light of the doorway looked annoyed. She was dressed in something resembling a Japanese kimono. It was very short and held together by her hands. It barely closed across her breasts. She wore no make-up. She was barefooted. She yawned.

"What is it you want?" she said harshly.

That voice identified her positively. It was Kiki.

"I'm sorry," I mumbled. "I didn't mean to wake you up."

"Then why were you knocking?"

I couldn't think of anything to say. I stared down at her naked feet.

"*Entrez!*"

It was an order. I stepped into the room. Except for the glass ceiling, the place looked more like a middle-class living room than an artist's studio. Books and papers were arranged in exemplary order on a large table. In a corner stood a grand piano, covered with a red plush throw trimmed with gold pompons. In another corner there was a huge couch, the blanket in disarray. Evidently Kiki had been sleeping. There were several easels around the room, along with half-finished canvases and painter's utensils.

Kiki went to the couch.

"Sit down!" she said sharply, draping herself on the couch and reaching for a cigarette.

It was rather dark in the room. Twilight would soon settle over the city, and the sky above the roof-tops was dotted with light clouds.

"Do I know you?"

My eyes had been still glued to her feet. Now I looked up.

"From the Jockey. We danced together."

"You Edouard?"

"No."

"Albert?"

I shook my head.

"Then I don't know you," she said and stretched herself out to recline on the couch. She looked at me with enormous, slightly slanted dark eyes.

There was a feeling of sensuality in the room accentuated by the unmade couch and the heavy scent of l'Heure Bleue in the air.

"You knew I was alone?" she said unexpectedly.

"No," I said, too quickly.

"Of course you knew," she said and took a deep pull on her cigarette.

For a brief moment I contemplated a second lie but then decided: why not let her know the truth?

"*Alors, mon gugusse,*" she said watching me carefully. "What is it you want?"

She looked at me. In the half darkness her pupils dilated and glistened.

I said the half-truth: "I wanted to buy one of your paintings."

"Mine?"

"Of course."

"Not Bernard's?"

"Who's Bernard?"

It occurred to me that I had never known the name of her lover.

"Bernard is my *régulier,*" she said. "He's a great artist. Here—" she made a wide sweep with her arm and her kimono opened to reveal a naked breast. "These are all his paintings."

Her whole face welcomed my gaze. Then, slowly, she drew the kimono together.

"I'm not interested in him," I said. "I wanted to buy one of your paintings."

"How do you know I am painting?"

"Everyone knows."

"Everyone?"

"Gitche Manitou told me about it," I said.

"What did he tell you?"

"He said they're exquisite."

She emitted a raucous laugh and gave her body a violent upward pull. She was on her feet, shaking her hair and roughing it with her fingers. Then, prompted by some inner urgency, she moved around the studio much like a restless cat. She struck a match and turned on the gaslight.

"If you want to see my drawings, we'll need light, won't we, *jeune homme?*" she said. "I will show them to you, but you cannot buy them. Not now. There will be a *vernissage*. At Botin's."

Moving, tossing her hair again, she lifted up a big folder. Taking out a number of drawings, she put them around on the easels and the furniture, and soon her entire *oeuvre* was spread all over the studio in an impromptu one-woman show.

"No one has seen them yet," she said, "—except Bernard."

She was watching my reaction. I inspected each drawing carefully, with professional pretense. Unschooled as I was, the originality of her work in pen and ink made an impression on me. Each drawing told a simple story, and there was an artless quality that was genuinely appealing.

"They're beautiful!" I said.

"You really think so?" She was surprised.

"I truly think so."

76

"And people will really buy them?" She seemed to doubt it.

"If I had enough money, I'd buy them all," I said.

There was a glow in her eyes, then, suddenly, recognition.

"Now I remember," she said, and came very close. "You gave me once fifty francs!"

I nodded happily.

"You were with those two *morues*!"

"And you made a date with me for the next day, but you never showed up!"

"You mustn't be bothered about that, *ma petite grue*," she said. "I guess I was ginny. I sometimes make a dozen dates when I'm ginny."

"But would you make a date with me *now*—"

"No, *mon petit*, I cannot." She cut me off. "I have Bernard, you know, don't you? And he is as jealous as a *coq*. You must leave now. He'll be back any moment."

She pushed me toward the door.

I was still clutching my brother's twenty-dollar check.

"Here," I said proudly. "Twenty dollars. I really meant to buy one of your paintings."

"Twenty dollars!" Kiki repeated. "Let me see."

She took the check out of my hand and studied it with some amusement.

"How much is this in francs?"

I mentioned the figure.

"Fouchtra!" she exclaimed. "You will pay that much for my drawings?"

"They're worth much more!"

"Zut! Tu est un drole de mironton!"

She handed me back the check. We were at the door. She gave me a playful shove: *"Au revoir, mon chou.* And hold on to your dollars. See you at the *vernissage."*

I was silent.

She waited for me to leave, her hand on the door knob. I gave way to an impulse I was powerless to squelch: I reached out and drew her close. For a moment her body strained backward, but then she closed her eyes and seemed to welcome my embrace.

I pressed my lips on hers. Her mouth was somewhat unexpected—a thrilling physical fact, disturbing and overwhelming, of what seemed to me an almost indecent intimacy.

After a while she disengaged herself from my embrace.

"You kiss well," she said, rearranging her open kimono.

I was dazed. That I had really kissed her, that she stood before me as she was, was something I couldn't grasp.

My bewilderment coaxed from her one of the most delightful laughs. *"Fiche ton camp!"* she cried, and pushed me out of the room.

78

WITH unsteady legs, I stumbled giddily down the stairs. I still couldn't quite believe what had happened—the extent of my audacity. I had really kissed Kiki. I felt light and happy. Her bare arms around my neck, her body lightly pressed against me, her strong mouth on my own, her tongue moving against mine—all this held a promise of all the wonders I had dreamed of.

Memory has its own rules, and nostalgia doesn't go by the book—for some people it is the scent of a flower, a moonlit lake, a star-pitted summer sky, but for me it will always be a melancholy, chilly October evening that brings back with agonizing sweetness the supreme moment of my first conquest: this kiss and that blind walk down the stairs of the old house on Rue Vaugirard.

Then I went back to the Jardin du Luxembourg, dark now, except for the light of the Musée, where in those days the great paintings of the Impressionists hung. I walked the parkways for hours, kicking up the autumn leaves, feeling happy, filled with a serenity and confidence I hadn't known I was capable of.

79

Finally I went home and wrote a letter to Kiki. In that letter I told her that I was in love with her, that the reason I had given for my visit had been just a pretext, that I was in an agony to possess her. It was a long and awkward letter, and when I reread it the next morning, I had the good sense to tear it up in little pieces.

I had by that time been in Paris almost a month, and the Sorbonne had seen little of me. With a surge of guilty conscience, I asked my landlady to wake me in the morning at seven. She did as requested, pounding her fist against the door with a force astonishing in such a frail body.

"Réveillez vous, monsieur!" she called out in a voice that matched her fist.

Reluctantly I got up to be on time at some of the courses I was enrolled in. Afterwards, when I went to the library to try to do some serious reading, I felt an awful inclination to let my mind wander; my head felt empty, and I had an odd sensation of lightness at the back of my neck and a sort of fluidity in my limbs. It didn't take any formal reasoning, really, to figure it out. I could not concentrate on any school subject because my mind was now entirely given over to an extracurricular subject.

I should mention, at this point, an incident that took place one day while I attended a class in *La Poesie Romantique*—an incident which at the time appeared to be irrelevant but to which, later, I was forced to attribute a decisive importance. I had chosen a course given by one Professor Fauchet-Matignon, but I had not gotten around to attending a single one of his classes for the simple reason that they were scheduled at eight in the morning. Even on this, the first morning I finally reached the classroom, I was about a quarter of an hour late.

I entered the small, dark amphitheatre through the rear door, situated behind the uppermost row of benches, and tried to slide noiselessly into the last bench, usually occupied by late-comers. Professor Fauchet-Matignon was reciting some verse of Victor Hugo's in the suave, well-modulated voice one was prepared to expect from an educated Frenchman declaiming *La Poesie Romantique*:

> *Je t'aime, exil! Douleur, je t'aime!*
> *Tristesse, sois mon diadème.*

I was trying to get organized—unfolding my notebook, taking pencil in hand—when a familiar scent came to my nostrils. You might expect to smell almost anything in a room dedicated to dust, chalk, files books, papers, but not Guerlain's l'Heure Bleue.

With a vague sensation of uneasiness, I looked up and found the source of the scent. It was the young woman sitting next to me, listening with deep absorption to the professor's recital. What first struck me about her was a certain similarity to Kiki in her upturned face. She had her hair cut in Kiki fashion and the Kiki kind of handsome nose and white skin. I could not be certain about her height, but from her slender figure and her long legs I concluded that she was tall. She certainly was not the kind of girl you'd expect at eight in the morning in a Sorbonne classroom. What little I had observed before of my female colleagues had looked dull, predictable, and unwashed. This one, however, looked very unpredictable and very washed. She was further distinguished by her attire: she wore a smart wool dress, sheer hose, and high heels.

Sideways I watched her. She was absorbed in Professor Fauchet-Matignon's recitals of Hugo — but it wasn't the absorption of a student. She seemed detached from the class. A small, preoccupied smile hovered about her lips as she looked over the heads of the others at the small figure of the lecturer on the dias. And now I discovered that the voice of the professor was geared to travel over the heads of the listeners in the amphitheatre toward the last row. Yes, he seemed to be addressing himself solely to the woman on my right, reciting Hugo exclusively for her. Even a deaf man would have noticed it.

"Je voudrais n'être pas Français pour pouvoir dire
Que je te choisis, France, et que dans ton martyre
Je te proclame, toi que ronge le vautour
Ma patrie et ma gloire et mon unique amour!"

I had up to that moment not paid much attention

82

to the lecturer, but now, because of what I was sure was a kind of contact between him and my neighbor, I fixed my gaze upon him.

Professor Fauchet-Matignon was a small man. His skin was bad—the color a uniform yellowish-brown, looking as if it still bore the remains of an attack of jaundice. His eyes were notable: very large and round, appearing even larger and rounder through the heavy lenses of his spectacles. His sharply receding chin bore a deep dimple in the center. As far as I could judge, he was close to sixty. What was the connection between the two, I wondered, turning my eyes again toward my neighbor; was she, possibly, his daughter?

She must have become aware of my scrutiny, for now she turned her face in my direction and her eyes rested briefly upon me. I thought she looked rather troubled, and her evasive glance suggested a state of mind both frightened and shy. It was an irregular face, but a beautiful one.

As quickly as she had looked at me, she turned her eyes away and concentrated again on the dais. Professor Fauchet-Matignon had finished reciting Hugo. His tone of voice changed to that of a lecturer as he spoke now, soberly, in a dry monotone: *"Hugo, après Chateaubriand et en même temps que Lamartine, a eu le sentiment d'un rapport entre la nature et l'homme . . ."*

There was rustling of notebooks.

I, too, tried to concentrate and jot down notes, but found it difficult to follow the lecture. Again my mind strayed. I began to doodle on the greenish paper.

A strong whiff of the perfume roused me from my daydreams. *"Excusez, Monsieur—"* a voice whispered. My neighbor had moved close to me, her body half-raised. I sat at the corner; she could not step out of the row until I made room for her to leave.

I rose. She squeezed her way out, her body brushing mine. Our faces were very close. She smiled a reticent, apologetic smile. And then she tiptoed to the exit door. I watched her go. For a brief moment she stood at the door and then, shyly, raised her hand and waved.

It was a deceptive gesture. She could have been waving at me, because I was still standing up and looking toward her. I turned crimson. But then the blush of pleasure quickly faded, for I clearly saw that her wave was not meant for me: I just happened to be standing in her field of vision.

When I turned around, I saw Professor Fauchet-Matignon looking up at her from his notes. He flashed an answering, parting smile.

She opened the door very carefully. Only then did I notice that she was much taller than Kiki. And while she was delicate from the waist up, her hips and legs were solid, strong, adult, full of muscular energy and swing.

When she had left, I returned to my doodling. The voice of the professor went on like the droning of a faraway bee swarm. I thought for a while about that beautiful girl and who she might be, and my curiosity was aroused enough to return the next morning to the lecture, but there was no sign of her.

For a whole week I attended this course, but she didn't return. I decided that she had just been a one-time visitor—possibly someone from out of town, a friend or relative of the professor's—and I dismissed her from my thoughts.

GUILTY about having wasted so much time, I tried to set to work and lead the life of a student, but whatever I did during the hours spent at the Sorbonne was merely an exercise in self-deception. I listened, jotted down notes, read books, but my head was filled with all the wild notions of the daydreamer.

Since my visit to Bernard's studio and our brief embrace, there had been a subtle change in my relationship with Kiki. Night after night I returned to the Jockey just to see her, just to share the same ambience with her for a short hour. It seemed to me that she always looked for me before she started with her songs and that when she discovered me her eyes rested seductively upon me. Maybe it was my imagination, but I thought there developed between us a certain conspiracy, a plot against her friend, and sometimes I even speculated whether I might not succeed in making her leave him for good. At such moments I said to myself that if a man loves a woman with all his heart, with all his thoughts, she cannot possibly refuse him.

But while I waited, I suffered, just as any lover does who knows the object of his desire belongs to someone else. I became the stock victim of jealousy. More than once, I followed Kiki and Bernard when they left the Jockey in the early morning hours and returned to their studio in the Rue Vaugirard. Both drank heavily, and in that state of "ginnyness" they staggered home through the streets as though dazed. I was sure it never occurred to them that they were being followed; I stayed so close to them that I not only observed their movements, but could listen to their lovers' talk. Kiki held her friend's hand with her fingers between his, as if rehearsing the expected interlacing of their bodies. Often they would stop suddenly and embrace, kissing each other furiously.

One night, nearing dawn, he held her in his arms and she drew back her head and breast—at the same moment lifting her dress. Since she never wore anything underneath her dress, her naked body came starkly into view. She thrust her belly forward toward Bernard, inviting love in plain view, regardless of who might see them. Bernard seized her roughly by the elbows and made her lower her dress, and then they continued on their way, swaying, laughing, kissing. Reaching home, they had to ring for the concierge. I stood on the opposite side of the street until they disappeared and the lights came on in the studio apartment. In my inflamed imagination, I calculated to the minute what went on upstairs. At this moment she was throwing off her dress. At that moment, naked, she was walking to the couch in the corner, getting on it, lying down. Now he would join her. The lights went out. Now they did the sweet thing. In the darkness, standing in shameful frustration in the moonlit street, I endured the whole shape and rhythm of their sexual act.

Yet in a way I enjoyed this suffering. I was young, and hopeful that eventually I too would be approaching that tantalizing, glittering summit.

Toward the middle of November, posters appeared all over Montparnasse, announcing the one-man show of Kiki's drawings. On the night I first noticed the posters, Kiki stopped by me as she made her rounds at the Jockey, collecting money, and whispered, "There will be a private preview, *mon petit*. I hope to see you." I just nodded, my pulse racing.

I had in the meantime cashed the twenty-dollar check for francs and put the money away in a sealed envelope marked "Kiki." The afternoon of the preview I dressed carefully, tore open the envelope, took the stack of money, and set out for Botin's in the Rue Cardinal Lemoine.

Botin's was one of the many small art places mushrooming in the Quarter. The prevailing trend in those days was toward surrealism, and I wondered how critics and viewers would evaluate Kiki's naive, Douanier-Rousseau-like drawings — so simple, so primitive, so artless compared to the hollow blocks of the cubistic school.

It was about one hour after the announced opening time, and when I entered Botin's I thought I had, by mistake, stepped into the Jockey. There was the usual mob scene and the complete cast of characters I had come to know by now, if only through rubbing elbows with them: the six Icelandic giants, rumored to be painters, who always stood at the bar in a state of drunken rigidity; Kling-Klong, the middle-aged satyr in kilts and plus-fours, his head shaved like a billiard ball; Raymond the Greek in his toga and sandals; the Georgian princess who taught new forms of body dynamics and held readings from her own sacred scriptures; the Japanese painter Foujita, who had done a number of paintings of Kiki, one of which had won a prize at the Salon de Paris.

Monsieur Botin, distinguished by a red carnation in his buttonhole and a dissipated face, circulated about the room like an industrious octopus, shaking hands, making introductions, manipulating the champagne bottles to fill glasses. People stood in clusters, drinking and laughing, and their conversation was a multilingual, often incoherent jumble of sounds. Kiki's drawings covered the walls but, amazingly, no one seemed to be looking at them. In fact, the impression grew in me that I had come to some cocktail party and not to the tensely awaited premiere of a new

89

painter. Looking for Kiki, I eventually discovered her in a corner of the gallery, surrounded by a coterie of men, prominent among them a world-famous Russian baritone who once in a while spent the early hours of the morning at the Jockey.

Kiki looked ravishing.

She wore a black silk evening dress, low-necked and sleeveless, and over her arm she held a fur cape. Her face was round and smooth, and she was laughing with such candor, so effortlessly; her wonderfully expressive dark eyes shone more brightly than ever. There was tonight a complete transformation of her physical appearance. She had just lit a cigarette someone had given her, and she was about to say something which her mind had already formulated but which had so far reached only her eyes.

I thought she had never been so much alive and so desirable as that evening. I could feel my face redden at the sight of her and—like an intruder—was undecided what to do or where to turn.

Someone grabbed me by the arm. It was Botin. "Wouldn't you like to meet the artist?" he asked me and cast an affectionate look across the room at Kiki.

"I'd love to. But shouldn't I see the drawings—"

"Of course, of course!" the little man said busily. "But first you must meet Madame Kiki and have a glass of champagne."

Not waiting for my consent, he maneuvered me

90

with great dexterity toward the group encircling Kiki.

"Madame Kiki," he cried—and I was embarrassed by the silliness of this semi-social, semi-commercial introduction— "may I present one of your admirers?" He hadn't even asked for my name.

When she recognized me, she gave me a dazzling smile and greeted me like one of her intimates: "*Ah, mon petit chopin!* Did they give you champagne? And did you bring your dollars?"

I stared at her in bewilderment. Her words gave me a feeling of acute pain, pain such as a man might feel who sees some gift, for which he has faced bitter sacrifices, despised and ridiculed. Of course I had brought the money—I wanted to say so in an impulse of rage and humiliation — but she didn't wait for an answer. To greet me, she had interrupted a joke she was telling, and now she went right back to finishing it. The Russian singer threw an arm around her and howled.

No one paid the slightest attention to me. I had decided once more to look at the drawings when I noticed a towering figure leaning against the wall.

It was Gitche Manitou, immaculately dressed in a dark suit. I elbowed my way over to him.

"I'm so glad to see you," I said. "You're the only friendly face in this room."

"You know Kiki, of course," he said diffidently.

"Yes, I've met the 'artist,' " I said, not without a touch of irony.

"And have you seen her work?"

"Yes," I answered, getting red. I had never told the Indian about my visit to Bernard's studio.

"And you like it?"

"I think she's quite remarkable."

"At least you can recognize what you see," Gitche Mantiou said. "They are full of a sense of play—like children much-loved. I meant to buy one drawing, but they were already gone."

"You mean some of her pictures have already been sold?"

"Didn't you notice the stars on the frames? The gold stars? It means they're already gone."

"How many have been sold?"

"*All* of them," Gitche Manitou said.

"ALL of them?" I asked in genuine confusion. "But how is that possible?"

"The preview started at five," Gitche Manitou said impassively. "I arrived at five-thirty, and by then half of the things had had the gold star pinned on them. Then the great Fyodor," he nodded in the direction of the baritone, "he's bought the other half. Without even looking at them."

He looked calm, yet there was an inflection of bitterness in his voice. I felt cheated out of my purchase and at the same time somehow elated.

92

"What did they sell for?" I asked. "I meant to buy one myself."

"That little squirt, Botin, put such a dirt-cheap price on them it's revolting."

"But why?"

"He may have thought of her as a charming dilettante. The jackasses running these galleries have no opinions of their own. And she probably didn't get much encouragement from Bernard."

"How foolish!" I cried. "Her work is excellent!"

"I think so, too," Gitche admitted, then added, "Well, she'll know better next time. A thing like this doesn't happen often around here. To have sold the complete showing in a short hour! She's a *succès fou*. Quite amazing."

His expression said nothing, but I knew what he was thinking. The waif without shoes. The inexperienced girl, working for a pimp. The half-virgin, showing her bosom for the price of a pack of cigarettes. The ingenue, going to bed with an old clown. The woman who never had a room of her own. The *succès fou*!

We fell silent. Our eyes strayed toward the corner where she was holding court. She must have told another of her bawdy stories, for there was a roar of laughter around her. The Russian exploded a fresh bottle of champagne.

Then the circle opened, and Kiki made her way

over to us, holding aloft the overflowing champagne bottle.

"Did you hear, *chef?*" she cried and threw her arms in childish delight around the Indian. "I'm sold out!"

"Felicitations!" Gitche Manitou said.

Seeing the gentleness and sorrow of that copper face, I recognized the weakness of the good.

"And this one," she said, patting my cheek, "he was the first one to tell me I was a painter. And I will not forget it. I will do a drawing for you free. You will like that, won't you?"

It made me feel humble and happy, the way a child is who has received an unexpected gift. My eyes told her of my gratitude and she welcomed my gaze.

"Let us have a toast!" Kiki laughed. "We must celebrate. Where is your glass, *chef?*"

"You know I don't drink," he said evenly.

"I know, but tonight you must make an exception."

He shook his head.

"*Tu est constipé, mon vieux,*" she said chidingly. "So that leaves more for me and *mon petit là!*"

She poured from the bottle. "*Merde alors!*" she said. Then touching her glass to mine, she turned to the Indian. "*Et je t'emmerde également!*" she said with a raucous laugh.

I emptied the contents of my glass in one gulp. So did Kiki.

"And what are you going to do now, Kiki?" Gitche Manitou asked her gravely.

"Right now?"

"After this evening."

"The same as before."

"You'll still sing at the Jockey?"

"*Je ne suis pas déserteur!*"

"But you must paint."

"I will paint in the afternoon."

"You must not give up."

"No—don't worry, *grand chef*," she laughed. "I won't give up."

"They will pay you more from now on."

"It is not the money—" A proud, childlike smile crossed her face. "It is that I am a painter. I'm a painter now, *chef*," she repeated exultantly. "Can you imagine—and I did it all alone."

It was as if she couldn't believe it. She looked at Gitche Manitou for confirmation.

"You're doing fine, *ma petite cocotte*," the Indian chieftain said with the faintest hint of a smile.

The Russian singer called for her in his booming baritone. Before returning to him, she said to us, "We're all going over later to the *grande ouverture* at Madame Carnevali's. Why don't you two join us?"

I looked questioningly at the Indian chief. He didn't answer, but his disdainful expression spoke for him.

95

"Never mind, *chef*," Kiki said quickly. "I know what you think—besides, you've got to be at the bar. But maybe *mon petit ami*—?" She let the sentence go unfinished and, blowing me a kiss, made her way unsteadily back to her group.

"Who's Madame Carnevali?" I asked excitedly.

"She's a *madame*," Gitche Manitou said sharply. "You know what a *madame* is, don't you?"

I must have been a study in innocence, for Gitche Manitou said grimly: "A *madame* usually runs a whorehouse."

"I know what a whorehouse is," I stammered. "But I didn't know one was invited to openings."

"Well, this *madame* has a new angle," the chieftain went on. "She's opening a *maison close* — under municipal supervision. The mayor of Montparnasse gets a cut in the profits and gives it his official seal of approval. Probably has a permanent free pass to the establishment, too. Well, as far as I'm concerned, it's just another filthy, low-down bordello."

"But—what is Kiki going to do there?"

"She is a friend of Madame Carnevali's," Gitche Manitou said sarcastically. "You know what a *gobe-mouche* is? We Americans say sucker. Kiki is a *gobe-mouche*. She will lend her help to anyone, and to any wicked cause."

He seemed quite weary, like someone with a pain he couldn't show, someone about to be destroyed by his locked-in love. I was reminded of a fable my

96

mother had once told me, the parable of the Spartan boy who was hiding a fox under his coat. Being a Spartan, he could not permit himself to show pain. And he didn't move his face while the fox began licking him, first playfully, then taking little bites, and finally eating him up in earnest. I had never before understood the allegory, but now I thought I did.

I wanted to say something to comfort him, but just then he turned and walked rigidly away from me and out of the gallery.

BEFORE that evening I hadn't paid more than one or two curious visits to the part of our quarter where the brothels were. It was conveniently located, just a few minutes walk from my boarding house.

Officially the whorehouses of Paris opened their doors at two in the afternoon and remained open until two in the morning. Some of the girls lived in the upstairs rooms of the house, and some were picked up at the end of the workday by their pimps, to whom they turned over their earnings. The whorehouses of the Latin Quarter were considered lowest in status; the high-class brothels were in the Madeleine, Opera, and Bois de Boulogne districts. But the girls on the Left Bank made about the same money, because business was thriving and the turnover was bigger. A lot of girls preferred these smaller houses to the phonily plush establishments of the Right Bank, for there they had to look well-groomed and watch their grammar. They felt more at home among the students, artists, and small businessmen who patronized houses in the Latin Quarter.

All this and other piquant details I learned from

Jules Ledieu, the son of Madame Ledieu, the proprietress of the *crémerie* on the corner of the Boulevard St. Michel and the Rue d'Odessa. The *crémerie* had become a hangout of mine, and Jules, who helped his mother in her business, was my confidant. He was a year younger than I, but a hundred years older in worldly wisdom. He knew every girl in every whorehouse of the Rue d'Odessa, and he could describe each one of them and her specialties with the intriguing persuasion of an Arabian storyteller. I listened with fascination to the tales of his sexual deeds which would be, so I tried to convince myself, either foreign to my nature or not within my capacity. To camouflage my inexperience I invented a girl friend who left me no time nor appetite for other amorous exploits, but I doubt if Jules believed me.

Wasn't he afraid of catching a venereal disease, I asked him one day. He certainly was, but he seemed to have found an ingenious solution to this ever-present threat.

Every Monday noon Dr. Arnault, the public medical inspector, made the tour of the houses in the Rue d'Odessa to examine *les filles*. They either got a clean bill of health for the week or were forbidden to take on clients. In the latter case they had to report to the hospital in the district.

The moment Dr. Arnault had finished his rounds and stepped into his carriage, Jules was on his way. Thus he was assured of being the first in the order of the day and reasonably certain not to catch a dose of the Morbus Gallicus.

But I still had a terrible fear of becoming diseased—a fear ingrained in me by my father. And it was this fright that made me stay away from the houses of ill repute which were so much a part of Parisian life in the Twenties. Yet while I kept away, the temptation to break down and look behind the closed shutters of the Rue d'Odessa was powerful, and my imagination was kept aboil by the lurid tales of Jules Ledieu. To justify my cowardice I told myself that I had to keep chaste for my eventual liberation, which I knew was now within grasp.

After leaving Kiki's exhibit at the gallery Botin, I went to the Dôme and had a ham sandwich at the bar in order to get some more information on Madame Carnevali's establishment. I learned that the new whorehouse was called "The Sphinx," and invitations to the *grande ouverture* had gone out to everyone who was anyone in the sixth borough. The unusual feature of the opening was that Madame had handwritten the invitations and had asked all addressees to feel free to bring their wives along.

When I arrived in front of the Sphinx, which was bedecked with a neon sign similar to the one on the Jockey, there was a wild crush to get inside. The whole quarter seemed to have turned out for the celebration. The champagne was on the house, and

100

the municipality had provided police protection to keep out party crashers.

At the entrance to the main salon stood the proprietress, a woman of formidable proportions. She greeted everyone with studied ceremony: a polite "Monsieur" or "Madame" or "Messieurs-Dames." Madame Carnevali looked more the part of a Wagnerian opera star than the madame of a whorehouse. She was a gigantic hulk of fat; hundreds of tiny blood vessels in her face and arms had broken down and become discolored with the sheer volume of fluid they had to carry. To help support her mammoth body she leaned on a large, silver-headed cane. Incongruously, her facial features were tiny.

Having passed her sharp-eyed inspection and having received a moist handshake, I entered the Sphinx.

Inside, I was welcomed by one of the dozens of girls who, as I learned, had been imported by Madame Carnevali from parts unknown and for some of whom this, too, was a "First Night." They were, as I could judge in the rose-colored light, young and demure and overawed by all this splendor. Also, they were tremendously impressed by "les artistes." They were simply dressed in long, flowing skirts of gauzelike material with brief panties underneath—obviously in keeping with the Egyptian note the house name suggested. From the waist up, the girls wore nothing. Madame Carnevali must have made her selection carefully, with an eye to that portion of the anatomy, for all the girls—tall or short, skinny or plump—displayed firm and enticing breasts.

The girl who poured champagne for me was blonde, and her bosom was awe-inspiring. I don't think she was older than sixteen. She told me her name was Mireille, and she came so close that her nipples touched me. Would I like to sit down with her and have some more champagne? Would I care to go upstairs and see the *chambres d'amour* or the room of special *divertissement?* Would I prefer just a "little moment" or maybe half an hour? She rattled down the whole "menu" of the Sphinx, complete with the price scale, but I had the feeling that she was as little experienced as I. Seized by uncertainty, I told her that I might avail myself of her offer later, but that right now I had come to join a friend of mine, a lady who had invited me. This brought an instant chill to her eyes. She turned away from me to welcome other guests and I was left alone.

The decor of the Sphinx bore no similarity to the image of the bordellos in my hometown or the houses in the Rue d'Odessa, none of the red plush and the heavy draperies that were standard equipment. Save for the subdued lighting, everything in the Sphinx looked "modern" and functional: an "American Bar" with a Negro mixing the drinks; a four-man band, blaring out foxtrots and Charlestons; even the uniformity of the girls' breasts seemed part of the plan. The place was packed, yet, oddly, the atmosphere was rather formal. There were a number of embarrassed-looking married couples who probably felt out of place among the whores and artists; then there were all the familiar faces I encountered every night—happily sponging the free champagne.

I heard glass crashing on the floor and the raucous laughter of Kiki. She sat at the head of a large table, surrounded by her usual coterie. A battery of empty bottles on the table was arranged in a bowling formation. Someone had unscrewed one of the round metal fixtures to use as a bowling ball. Crash!—and more bottles splintered on the floor.

Kiki was drunk, as was the rest of the group, but she seemed thoroughly and completely happy. I had seen her "ginny" on several occasions, but I had never seen her drunk. It was painful to watch, and I wanted to leave.

But just then she recognized me and jumped up to catch my elbow. I was sorry she had seen me. "Where are you going?" she cried. "Come over—meet my *copains.*"

In shame and bewilderment I followed her. "This is my little friend—" she yelled. "And these—" she made a sweeping gesture, "—these are my good *copains!*"

Everyone else was drunk, too. Kiki emptied a

103

bottle into a glass and made me drink, and I gulped down all of it with a sense of repugnance. How is it possible, I thought, for her to disgrace herself in front of all these pimps and prostitutes and poseurs? And how could Bernard permit her to make a fool of herself; he loved her, didn't he? There he was, his arms around Kiki's bare shoulders, kissing her behind the ears with what seemed to me unnecessary vulgarity.

All the while the bowling game went on. Kiki forced the metal ball into my hand and urged me to take my turn; without any real skill I knocked the remaining champagne bottles off the table. There were shrieks of laughter and applause, and Kiki flung her arms around me and kissed me on the cheek. But while I felt the breath of her lips against my cheek, I was almost repelled by this intimacy, the more so because Bernard showed no signs of resentment.

A couple of girls came to the table and filled our glasses. A blissful haze enveloped me. Like that night when I had passed out at the Jockey, I drifted into a pleasant void. I heard voices, but there was no meaning to the words. Behind clouds I saw the enormous frame of Madame Carnevali leaning down and talking to Kiki. And then I heard Kiki's voice. She stood in the center of the rectangular room under a spotlight and she sang,

> *Amis, copains, versez à boire.*
> *Versez à boire et du bon vin*
> *Je m'en vais vous conter l'histoire*
> *De Caroline la putain.*

Bernard nudged me. "She's never sung that," he whispered. *"C'est un peu fort de café mais une vraie goutte!"* He leaned forward on the table, staring at her with ugly bulging eyes.

> *Elle perdit son pucellage*
> *Le jour d'sa première communion*
> *Avec un garçon de son âge*
> *Derrière les fortifications.*

"Derrière les fortifications!" —everyone chimed into the chorus.

> *A vingt-quartre ans, sûr ma parole,*
> *C'etait une fière putain.*
> *Elle avait foutu la vérole*
> *Aux trois quarts du Quartier Latin.*

"Aux trois quarts du Quartier Latin—" they bellowed back.

I was far gone, but not far enough to join. Someone poured me another glass of champagne, but I pushed it away and the glass crashed on the floor.

Kiki had finished the song, and the band began the

Charleston, the dance which had just invaded the continent. Bernard got up and weaved over to the dance floor. "Charleston — Charleston!" A circle formed around Kiki and Bernard as they both, not touching each other, kicked their heels back and went into a furious performance of the dance. "Charleston! Charleston!" Their gyrations became wilder, their knees knocking and then pushing apart. "Charleston! Charleston!" the audience yelled.

Watching them, I was deeply resentful. It was foolish and unrealistic to pass moral judgment, but I was foolish and unrealistic. Didn't she sing the same kind of songs nightly at the Jockey? I asked myself. Didn't she dance the Charleston there, and didn't she lift the skirts so you could almost see the dark between her legs? Yes, but here she seemed to defile herself. Here she was performing to stimulate business in a whorehouse. It seemed to me a terrible loss of grace, and I wished I had never seen her or come to that whorehouse.

The air turned thick. My legs were heavy, and I sank into a chair. There was a commotion at the entrance. More and more people had tried to squeeze into the Sphinx, and I saw that the doors were closed. Kiki came back to the table and flopped down. "*Fouchtra!*" she cried. "I'm thirsty." "Champagne!" the Russian baritone roared, and two girls came rushing to the table with fresh bottles. One of them was Mireille.

Kiki looked at me with glassy eyes, eyes that seemed to have difficulty in focusing. *"Alors, toi—"* she said in her hoarse vocie. "You don't look happy. What is it? *Peut-être tu a besoin de faire un petit truc?"* I stared at her uncomprehendingly. Kiki laughed and looked up at Mireille: *"La voila—la petite—elle va faire une belle jambe pour toi! N'est-ce pas, Mireille?"*

Mireille offered a wicked smile, and suddenly I understood. And as I understood, I forced a grin and at the same time I felt the kind of deep shame that sweeps from head to foot and through all the nerves and fingers and intestines and glands. Kiki was acting as a procuress for Madame. She had offered Mireille to me.

Mireille waited for my decision. I did not wish to show any of the anxiety I felt. So I made a sort of inner surrender to the situation. I said: "Sure. Why not? Let's go up!" And as I said it, I detected—or was I wrong?—a faint hint of regretful surprise cross Kiki's face.

However, there was nothing to do now but go through with it. I grabbed the blonde girl by the hand and headed for the stairway.

"One moment—" Mireille stopped me. "You must

pay first. Madame Josette!" she called and a middle-aged woman, the assistant hostess, rather conservatively dressed, came over.

"Monsieur would like to have a little visit with Mademoiselle Mireille?"

My mouth went dry.

"Mireille est extremement gentille et caressante," Madame Josette assured me. "You would like *une petite demi-heure?"*

"I guess so," I answered numbly.

The assistant hostess named the price for the *demi-heure* and I paid, and then Mireille took me by the hand and led me towards the upstairs room. I was glad she led me, because all strength seemed to have gone out of my legs.

Upstairs was a long, softly lighted corridor. The streamlined character of the Sphinx was reflected even here by the presence of red and white bulbs above the doors, indicating the occupancy or availability of rooms.

By the time we had reached a door with a white bulb, I was in a blue funk. Sweat gathered on my forehead. Mireille's hand, still holding mine, was also moist, as if my timidity and fear had communicated itself to her. We entered the room like characters in some sordid tragedy.

Two towels, lying on the chair, were the first

things I noticed. There was also a huge bed, a bidet, and a wash basin with running water. Mireille, wordlessly, pulled me over to the bed while I just stared in terror at the two towels. The effect of the whole thing was one of grayness and despair.

Mireille sat down and with a kind of clumsy directness drew me to herself, twisting her bare nipples against my shirt.

"Won't you take off your things?" she whispered in a shaky voice.

I kept silent.

"*Eh bien,*" she said. "I will."

There wasn't much she had to take off—the skirt, the panties, her shoes.

She stood naked, waiting for me to undress. She had a beautiful body, but I felt I was not looking at a real person; it was more like seeing a machine made of flesh. I hadn't the faintest desire to embrace her. And this naked stranger, obviously a novice to her profession, did nothing to make things easier for me. When I made no move to touch her, she shrugged slightly and sat down on the open bed.

I stood motionless, feeling paralyzed. She lay on her back, her arms across her eyes. She spread her legs apart and then stayed that way without moving. I was rooted, staring down at a cold, waxen whiteness. This picture I still have with me, after all these years, this lifeless picture of a body, not only because of the deathly pallor of her skin, but because of the prolonged stillness in the room.

Eventually she took her arm off her eyes and said: "What is it? Am I that ugly? What are you waiting for?"

There was such bitterness and hostility in her voice that my own coldness evaporated, giving way to a flush of shame. I had wounded her deeply. By not touching her I had conveyed to her that she was not worth a touch. That she was not a woman. That she was nothing but an inexperienced whore.

Suddenly I felt the threat of tears and, unable to utter a single word of kindness, I turned and rushed out of the room.

OUTSIDE it was raining.

Rain hissed down from an opaque sky and spread darkness everywhere. It poured down in one direction and then, as the wind changed, in another, and it ran from my hair down my neck and then inside the shirt, down my back. Intermittently there was the brilliance of a lightning flash.

I was filled with an inner agony for which I could find no outward expression.

Without knowing where my feet were taking me, and not caring, I found myself in the middle of the Pont Royal, which spans the Quai Voltaire and the Tuileries. I stared down at the swollen, muddy torrent and for a moment thought of suicide.

It is easy to smile in retrospect at those foolish impulses of our adolescence. But reliving that night, seeing myself standing in the black nowhere of the Pont Royal, I don't find that impulse absurd: at that moment my whole outlook was clouded by a feeling of helplessness and pain.

The only sound in the night was that of the rain and the water gurgling below.

Startled at the touch of a hand on my soaked back, I turned to find a policeman facing me. I felt caught in some act I hadn't committed. The *flic* looked at me with friendly eyes, as if reassuring me that he was not a law-enforcing power tonight, but simply an understanding passerby who wanted to restrain me from doing anything rash.

Looking at his warm face, I was reminded of my father, and the thought of him started me sobbing. I wept at my betrayal of him, at the shiftless confusion of my life, at my self-indulgence, and at the kindness of the *flic*.

Without trying to understand my troubles, he consoled me with his presence and a few words of encouragement.

Collecting myself, I thanked him and started walking away from the bridge toward my neighborhood. I walked all the way home bareheaded through the deluge.

In my room I threw myself sorrowfully on the bed, feeling like a loosened violin string that could never be tight again.

Exhaustion put me to sleep.

When I woke late next morning, it was still pouring—the sky was joined in my sorrow. I went to the window and looked down upon the boul' Mich'; the rain seemed to have transformed the whole of Paris into water—buildings, pedestrians, lamp posts, and streetcars all flowed together as part of a liquid mass.

I sat down and my head started to work. I thought about Kiki and what to do about her, and my only reaction was one of impotence, of resignation. I told myself that my hope had been a mistake and my expectation an error. I had become the victim of a mass of childish fantasies; now it was time to find my way back to the kind of life I had promised myself and my parents to lead. I would work, I would read, and I would write. And I would never set foot in the Jockey again, or go near the Montparnasse places where I might be seduced into the kind of life that obviously was not meant for me.

But it wasn't as easy as all that. For the more deliberately I tried to blot out the image of Kiki, the more obstinately the sensuous memory of her imposed itself upon me. I thought of her more than ever, even though I kept one promise I had made to myself and stayed away from Montparnasse. I clung to the few moments of intimacy I had hoarded, and the memory of the kiss she had given me.

My only escape during this time was sleep. The minute I came home from classes or a walk along the boulevard, I stretched out on my bed.

When I tried to listen to lectures, I sank into a dreamless, waking unconsciousness. Or, with my eyes fixed on a table where books waited to be studied, I

113

dozed off in a chair. Sometimes I lay asleep till late in the afternoon, and often I didn't even make an effort to get up for meals. It was a morbid flight from reality; under the corrosive sadness of resignation, even the slightest physical move was an effort.

The weather was still bad. For days a thin, irritating rain kept the city blotted out from light.

Then one morning I woke with a mild, pleasing excitement. It was still early and I remembered it was Thursday, the day of the *Poesie Romantique* class. The sun had dried the wet faces of the houses that I looked out on from my windows.

For the first time, I went outside not feeling blue and crushed. The weather mirrored my change of mood: with the sun out and the air smelling freshly washed, the boulevard was alive with people.

Entering the University I glanced up at the sundial which dominated the south side of the courtyard. *Horas non numero nisi serenas,* read the inscription: I count only the happy hours. The dial pointed at eight. And then, as my eyes traveled downward, I stopped. In all that stir of people hurrying along, in all that electric morning activity of students trying to reach their classrooms on time, there stood the solitary figure of a man who obviously didn't belong there. He stood right under the sundial, almost as rigid as the statues of Pasteur and Hugo that flanked him. It was Gitche Manitou.

114

"Hello, Chief!" I said.

He gave me a level and meaningful look.

"Well," he said after a long pause. "Finally—there you are!"

"Yes. Here I am," I repeated dumbly. "But what are you doing here?"

"I don't know where you live—so I could think of only two ways to find you," the Indian said. "Go to the police or look for you among the students. So I've been hanging around here. It's been very enjoyable. If I could start all over again, this is the place I would choose to start."

A vague smile appeared on his lips.

"I'm on my way to class," I said, not quite knowing what was expected from me. And then on a sudden impulse: "Would you like to come along?"

He seemed incredulous.

"I could—?"

"Certainly. I'll take you along."

He followed me into the somber corridors of the University with modest, hesitant steps. I decided to use the back entrance to the classroom, where the presence of a stranger would not create any undue attention.

The lecture had started, and as we tiptoed to our seats, I looked around to see whether I could find the strange girl that I had seen once. But all I saw were the drab and sleep-drunk faces of my fellow students, some of which I had come to know by now, if only at a distance.

Professor Fauchet-Matignon's morning lecture was devoted to Musset. As was his routine, he was reciting samples of the writer's work; I marveled at such perceptive delivery of poetry by a man so lacking in outward grace. There he stood, a small pathetic figure with yellowish skin, yet Alfred de Musset's verses wafted through the auditorium like strains of music.

L'amour est tout—l'amour, et la vie au soleil
L'amour est le grand point, qu'importe la maîtresse
Qu'importe le flacon pourvu qu'on ait l'ivresse?

But my own rapport with the world of Musset was tenuous compared to that felt by the Indian chief. He sat listening as if attending divine services, his face rapt. And the intense look of wonder and worship did not leave him during the whole hour, not even when the professor changed from his musical oratory to a matter-of-fact discourse on Musset's verse meter.

When the bell rang and Professor Fauchet-Matignon dismissed the class, Gitche Manitou turned to me unhappily, like a child who had been thrown into a temporary relationship with beauty and enchantment only to have the contact rudely broken off.

"What a wonderful experience!" he said as we

116

walked toward the courtyard. "You're so fortunate to be able to come here every day."

"You could do it more often," I told him. "I would gladly take you along. As far as I know, there's no age limit."

"If you remember your Plato, my young friend," he said to me in his low and earnest voice, "you will know what he said about Solon. 'Solon,' according to Plato, 'was under a delusion when he wrote that a man growing old may learn many things—for he can no more learn much than he can run much; youth is the time for any extraordinary toil.' "

Again his knowledge astonished me. In his attitude there was not the slightest resentment of people like me, to whom education and development would come more easily than to him. But I wondered about his obsession with age. He himself disproved Plato's dictum, for he was learning most in the autumn of his life.

We crossed the courtyard and reached the carved doors to the outside.

"Let's go somewhere we can talk," suggested Git-che Manitou. "I could use a strong cup of coffee."

We went to the corner of the Rue Souflot and the boul' Mich', to the Café de la Source. It was a pleasant place, clean and friendly and filled with students. We put our overcoats and hats on the rack above the

bench and ordered café au lait. The waiter brought a
basket with still hot croissants and we dunked them
into the coffee, and when we felt both relaxed and
warm, he asked in his even, unhurried way, "Where
have you been keeping yourself?"

I thought rapidly back. It had been just about a
month before that the Kiki exhibition had been held.
I hadn't been to Montparnasse since then. "I had to
study," I said evasively. "Evenings I was so tired I just
couldn't move."

He gave me a speculative look.

"Why don't you tell me the truth?" he said, pleasantly enough.

"It *is* the truth," I protested.

"You went to the whorehouse," he said unexpectedly. "Did you get yourself in trouble?"

The question made me feel guilty, though I
couldn't have said why.

"No, no—" I answered. "There was no trouble."

"Kiki was worried—"

"About me?

"Yes, about you."

My heart and spirit leaped.

"What did she say?'

"She said, 'Where is that *petite grue*? I've made
him a drawing. I want to give it to him.' "

My heart gave another bound. My resolutions of

118

renunciation were forgotten. All my hungry longings for her revived.

"Has she come to visit you?" I asked.

"Quite a few times lately," the Indian said. "She sometimes stays all afternoon and works."

"At your place? I don't understand."

"She's lost her studio," Gitche Manitou said slowly. "It's in the in-between times that she likes to come back to a place where she once found peace and quiet."

I was stunned. My expression must have amused him, for now he said: "Oh—I forgot to mention. She left Bernard."

She had left Bernard!

I let the wonder sink in. For a while we sat silent, and then I asked (and I was surprised at how routine, how calm, how detached my voice sounded), "What happened?"

"I think her success as a painter had a lot to do with it. As a model, Bernard made good use of her. As a competitor, he tired of her quickly."

"But you said that *she* left *him*?"

"Of course she left him. No one ever leaves Kiki."

"Is she very unhappy?'

"Unhappy? Kiki?" The Indian permitted himself a short laugh. "Kiki doesn't know the meaning of unhappiness. She came one afternoon and she

119

brought a bottle of gin. I've given Bernard the gate, *Chef*, she said, and she was laughing. I'm free, *Chef*. Let's drink."

"And when did all this happen?"

"Soon after the opening show. When all those fine reviews came out in the papers."

My God, I thought, she left Bernard weeks ago and I didn't know it—all that time, during which I had been immersed in self-pity, had renounced her, had resigned from the world. The realization made my mouth go dry. I had to wait for a while to quiet the wild thumping inside.

"And where does she live now?"

"With Chiffonette."

"How come?"

"Chiffonettee is an old friend of Kiki's."

"But you're an older friend. Why doesn't she live with you?"

"No—" Gitche Manitou said gravely. "That will never be again."

"But she comes to work in your room?"

"Sometimes. Like—" he paused and gave me a long, intense look— "like this afternoon!"

I had a surprising desire to cry.

"Would you let me visit you this afternoon?"

"If you still remember my address," Gitche Manitou said.

* * *

"You're a funny type," Kiki said that afternoon. "First I thought that little Mireille at the Sphinx had given you a dose of the old *douleur* but next day she told me no, you are a virgin, which has amused me much. *Saperlipopette!* I had never known! When I was your age I knew all about that business: I worked for a woman in the place Saint-Charles. Her husband was a baker. She gave me a mattress and food and thirty francs a month. Up at five in the morning to serve bread to the men on their way to work. At seven, I had to deliver bread, climb up and down all those flights of stairs—it was enough to break your back! Then I had to straighten up the house, run errands, and work in a flour closet. My duty there was to use a big iron bar to keep shoveling flour into a sifter. I'd come out of the closet white as a corpse. Also, I had to help the baker take the bread out of the oven. That rascal used to strip naked to work. He said it was too hot in the bakery, and he made dirty jokes for my benefit. Look, Alice, look, he'd say, you'll never see another one like that. He was hot for me, which was only natural considering his wife. She was a mean old frump, a vile-tempered witch. Anything she told me to do, she yelled her head off. One day I blackened my eyebrows with burned matches and she came with a wet towel to wipe it off. Then—well, it was just too damn much. I gave her a good beating, and when she yelled for

121

help, in came the patron and tried to separate us. I had her by the hair and he whispered to me, 'That's the stuff, Alice! Kiil her, that old witch!' But I did not kill her. I packed my things and beat it."

I was sitting on the floor of Gitche Manitou's room, leaning against a bookcase, listening with fascination. Mouchette lay curled up in my lap purring contentedly; we both watched Kiki, who stood in front of an easel, working on a drawing. Our host was stretched out on his couch, reading, looking up from time to time.

"*Alors, mon petit,*" Kiki said without turning her head. "How do you like this one?"

I looked at the work in progress. Like all her other sketches, it was of a childhood memory. She called it "Washer Women," and it was a robust evocation of her Burgundy days: a group of women rinsing their wash in the river and hanging it up to dry.

"I love it," I said.

"Ah," she said in mock anger, "you show no discrimination! You say of everything: I love it. I just want to know whether you *like* it. You like it better than the one I gave you?"

Earlier she had presented me with a charming sketch: children playing in a school yard, Kiki among them, in a little girl's checkered apron.

"I don't like it better than the one you gave me," I said, telling the truth.

"And why not?"

"The one you gave me has you in it," I said.

"Liar!" she cried, and gave me a playful slap on the cheek.

She moved restlessly around the easel, studied the sketch, made a face, then took the canvas and tore it up.

"It's no good," she said.

"But it was wonderful!" I protested.

"It was not. I must start all over again—some other day."

She went over to the window and, throwing it open, took several deep breaths of the damp winter air.

"What time is it, *Grand Chef?*"

"Half-past four," Gitche Manitou said. "Close the window. It's cold."

Kiki peered out of the window.

"I expect someone," she said.

"Who?"

"A painter. He is from South America. He wants me to pose."

"And you asked him to come up here?" Gitche Manitou raised his eyebrows.

"I gave him your address. He will come to pick me up. He is quite a *coqueluche*, this one. And he drives a car."

"Where did you meet him?"

"At Jimmy's," Kiki said. "Last night—or was it in the morning? Anyway, he's very amusing."

She laughed, and I felt a sting of jealousy. I had hoped she would stay and that she might accept an invitation to have dinner with me. I had never heard the word *coqueluche*, which somehow disturbed me, nor did I like the thought of an amusing South American with his own car.

Kiki was about to close the window when we heard the noise of a car pulling up below. "There he is!" she cried and leaned out over the window. *"Tout de suite!"* she yelled down, waving.

"Maybe I can make it tomorrow again," she said as she collected her painting equipment, folded the easel, and stored everything in the closet.

I helped her into her coat, and then she went over and bussed Gitche.

"Will you be at the Jockey tonight?" he asked.

"I don't know," she replied. "I'll see how the evening goes."

"Watch the *coqueluche*!" said Gitche Manitou without a smile.

"A chic type," Kiki said. "Brazilian!"

She grabbed her purse, a stupendously big one, and gave me a peck on the cheek. *"A tout a l'heure, mon petit chou,"* she said as if I were now an accepted intimate. "And do not make more trouble for us."

She had already opened the door to go out when the cat leaped onto her shoulder. It perched there, tail straight up and waving slightly. "Ah, Mouchette," Kiki cried. "I have not said *au revoir* to you." She pulled the cat off her shoulder and cradled it in her arms, smoothing its fur. Then she covered it with kisses.

The smell of l'Heure Bleue still clung to Mouchette long after the door behind Kiki had closed.

I went over to the window and looked down. Kiki had just stepped out onto the sidewalk. A man with a Burberry coat stood waiting at the door of a convertible. He was about thirty and distinguished by a little mustache. When Kiki stepped up to the car, he opened the door with ceremony and helped her in.

"What does *coqueluche* mean?" I asked Gitche Manitou.

"A *coqueluche* is a lady killer," he answered. "Something, I'm afraid, you're not." And he offered me one of his rare smiles.

"You're not a great help, Chief," I said forcing a grin in return. "Have you no word of comfort for me?"

"I have not," the Indian chief said placidly. "But our friend Plato has." He was looking past me as if to read an invisible inscription on the blank wall: " 'You are young, my son, and as the years go by time will change and even reverse many of your present opinions. Refrain, therefore, a while from setting yourself up as a judge of the highest matters.' "

THE South American *coqueluche* did a series of striking drawings, from Kiki the gamine to Kiki in the nude. One of his pictures entranced me so much that I stole it.

I could have just asked Kiki to let me have it, I suppose. But somehow when I saw it my hand seemed to acquire a mind and will of its own.

It was Kiki naked from the waist up. Her nipples stood taut, and about her parted lips there was such a powerful projection of sensuality that I responded as if she were in fact facing me, warm and naked. I slipped the drawing between the pages of a magazine, and the next day bought a frame and hung it above the desk in my room.

Gradually I had become one of Kiki's camp followers. I was admitted into the inner circle and was participating in the meeting of her elite.

These roving Montparnassians had three favorite watering places: the Café du Dôme, the Rotonde, and the Select. Life started around five-thirty. The habitués would begin to appear, seating themselves at separate single tables, slowly sipping their drinks, waiting for Kiki.

Her entrance was the cue for them to join her at the center table, which as a rule had a "reserved" sign planted on it.

It was known as Kiki's table.

There were other similar tables.

There was the painters' table, presided over by Pascin. Braque, Marcousssis, and Derain were the regulars; Utrillo, Matisse, and Picasso visited occasionally. Then there was the writers' table, with Ford Maddox Ford, Hemingway, Fitzgerald, Ezra Pound. James Joyce dropped in once in a while.

Memory evokes other human landmarks of the times: the monocled Tristan Tzara, leader of the Dadaists; the sad Alexander Berkman, who had emptied his revolver into the body of an American steel magnate; the "red" Russian, Ilya Ehrenburg.

When all of Montparnasse was aboil—around seven o'clock— the "Tourists" began to arrive: Americans in checked shirts, Scandinavians in sweaters and heavy boots, playboys in tuxedos, women in men's clothes, dipsomaniacs, dope fiends, schizophrenics, Hindu mystics: it seemed that the whole world had contributed its most extraordinary specimens, its most outrageous clothes, its most promising artisans to that incredible conflux at Metro Vavin.

Kiki's companions, except for occasional famous

127

visitors like Foujita, Kisling, or Man Ray, were mainly a disreputable bunch of revelers whose achievements were nil and whose virtues were doubtful. That is today's estimate, looking back at those winter evenings and nights. But I was young then, yearning to be part of the big world—it was there for me in Paris, in the Montparnasse world of Kiki.

During the brief time in her court, I learned that the most important thing was finding something to laugh about. Always there was the laughter—noisy, howling, wild. What was it about?

Nothing—everything.

There were always jokes to tell, Rabelaisian romances, Machiavellian plots, tales of infidelities, perversions, orgies. I listened to a language I didn't understand, though it was French. I still wonder how I was able to sit at those conclaves for hours, silent among strangers, trying to enter the spirit of laughter, the obscure allusions, the bon mots that were incomprehensible to me.

"Why do you look so gloomy, *ma petite grue?*" Kiki would ask me while she finished her sixth Pernod and I nursed my first. "Why don't you laugh?"

I would force a smile but it wouldn't be very convincing. How could I have made it clear to her that nothing that people around our table talked and laughed about had any real interest for me? That there was nothing to which I could attach my signature? I was the product of a staid middle-class background, and my only claim to "Bohemianism" was the ironic fact that Bohemia was my native land. Yet there was this urge to be one of the group, and more strongly there was my hunger for Kiki, a hunger that fed on her presence and grew with denial.

My mal d'amour was obvious to the group, of course, and occasionally someone would point at me and explode with a drunken remark to the effect that it was about time for Kiki to give in to me, to which Kiki would answer laughingly, "I can't stand him." At the same time she would cast at me a look of such lascivious promise that more than once I actually grew faint.

It was winter now, but the thermometer never fell below freezing; there was occasionally a thin layer of snow in the streets and parks, but it melted quickly in the feeble sunshine which appeared around noontime. The house I lived in was a relic of the Second Empire, and each room was heated individually. Mine had a small fireplace, in disrepair because it had never been used. I had it fixed and bought a generous supply of *boulets* — molded, egg - shaped lumps of coal that radiated a fine heat throughout the room.

Elsewhere, though, it was impossible to get warm and even harder to get dry. Dampness was everywhere and so was the common cold (as well as laryngitis, bronchitis, and pneumonia). In the poorly heated amphitheatres of the Sorbonne, the walls and stone floors exuded such bone-chilling moisture that the students huddled within their clothes, faces drained and sallow.

The coffeehouses were the one sure place to keep warm. In fact, they were overheated. So were the nightclubs and dancehalls of the Quarter.

In February, there was a ball every night: the policemen's ball, the servants' ball, the ball of the concierges. There was the ball of the midinettes, the St. Catherines, the mannequins. Good heating was essential because the participants were scantily dressed, and, as the night wore on, sometimes threw off what few clothes they came in to begin with. At the Quatz'Arts ball, for instance, men wore tuxedos and the women wore nothing. But perfect propriety prevailed, I was told by Jules Ledieu, who had wangled an invitation from one of his art student customers. (Only students and their models were admitted to the Quatz'Arts.)

The biggest event of the particular season was an invitational costume ball given by a notorious Paris hostess. Kiki was a member of the committee and submitted names of her friends whom she wished to be invited—and I was among them.

The thought that Kiki might choose me to accompany her kept me in a kind of euphoria throughout the whole week until, the day before the dance,

130

she told me that the South American would be her escort. I felt stabbed. "You don't understand," Kiki said quickly. "It is just that I have promised him. But don't worry—with you I will have every free dance." She pressed my hand with such warmth that my damaged feelings were repaired and my high spirits returned.

Balls and masquerades in those days seemed magic affairs at which one made exciting discoveries and lived through undreamed-of adventures. The very name "costume ball" was cloaked with mystery. It evoked the image of my mother, who had one night during my childhood appeared in my room for the usual good-night kiss, dressed in a sparkling white dress. The dress had a train and thousands of tiny silver stars. I felt an intoxicating pride in the transformation of my mother, and when she leaned down to touch my forehead with her lips, I was filled with a sense of wonder and reverence. It was also the first time that I became conscious of her femaleness. The bodice of the dress was cut low enough to show a division of her breasts. I asked her the reason for her disguise, and she whispered to me in a voice which didn't seem to belong to her that she was going to a ball and that she would be dancing there. With whom will you dance? With your father—and other men. It was that "other men" that was the only disturbing note in this otherwise harmonious vision, and for years I had a recurring dream in which my mother participated in some sort of bacchanalian orgy—surrounded by dancing satyrs.

After a great deal of thought about the kind of costume I would wear, I consulted my friend Jules.

He advised me to avoid an elaborate masquerade. He had once rented a suit of chain mail from a theatrical renting place and the evening had been a disaster, for not only had the visor of the helmet slammed shut, making him almost suffocate, but the armor had prevented him from getting a feel of the girls he danced with. "Just rent yourself a domino, *mon vieux*," he counseled me. "And underneath— nothing. That's the best!" This suggestion excited and at the same time repelled me; after discussing some more possibilities, we finally decided I should wear black tights, velveteen jacket, and a beret. The poet Rodolpho in *La Bohême* was much closer to the image I had of myself.

On the evening of the great ball, Jules came up to my room to supervise my costume. I had changed, he assured me, into a chic type, but lacked maturity. Quickly he burned a box of matches and painted an elegant mustache above my upper lip.

When I left the house, it was snowing; the flakes shone like iron filings in the beam of the street lamps. I felt exhilarated and walked all the way to the Bal Nègre in the Rue Blomet, a dancehall which had been taken over for the night.

At the entrance to the ballroom, I checked my coat

and muffler; my ticket of admission was inspected three times before I was permitted to enter the ballroom. The dancehall was ingeniously decorated, transformed into an oriental seraglio. The lighting was subdued, the orchestra played a waltz. Most of the guests were wearing masks, and they moved in a world of Arabian sheiks, maharajas, Napoleons, Carmens, Colombines, slave girls, fishwives; some girls wore just butterflies on their nipples or grass skirts around their loins.

I tried to find Kiki. A girl in pink tights grabbed me and seemed to offer not only her lips but her whole body. She pressed her mouth upon mine, and the smell of sour wine made me pull back. When I tried to free myself, she pushed me away and with a vulgar spate of drunken French dissolved in the crowd.

Another girl, this one in high heels, black stockings, and garters, put her hand boldly between my groins. Surprise, as much as anything, made me draw away from her as if I'd been stung.

As the waltz came to an end, the lights went out. The orchestra broke into a fanfare, and a spotlight illuminated a procession entering the ballroom.

At the head of it was Kiki. Leaving the garish costumes to others, Kiki wore a simple, low-cut dress. A deep red rose was clenched in her teeth. I had adored the look of her from the very first, but the beauty of her body that night was extraordinary. Her skin was lustrous, her eyes irridescent. As she marched by, a slight smile appeared on her face. Had she recognized me? As I asked myself the question, I received an answer: she took the rose and tossed it to me. I felt a rush of pride and gratitude. I followed her with my eyes as she led the parade in a circle, and when the music struck up again with a current tune, I slipped the rose into my buttonhole and worked my way toward her.

"Oh, how silly you look!" she cried when I caught up with her, but her look was glowing and the clasp of her hand reassuring. We started dancing, her body against me, her bare, cool arms around my neck. Her lips gently touched my cheek, her hair lightly brushed my neck and ears.

What had begun as a dance became a walk, a sway, as I embraced her body, feeling her breasts, her legs. I wanted to say more than *"Je t'aime,"* but all that escaped me was a half-choked *"—t'aime—t'aime—"* I closed my eyes and let the mood take over.

All of a sudden I embraced air. She was gone. I opened my eyes. Someone had danced away with her. It was the South American. He wore a black patch over one eye, a red bandana across his forehead. I felt castrated.

I went to one of the buffets and had a glass of champagne. A second glass, and I felt some of my confidence returning. I went back into the ballroom.

She was still dancing with the *coqueluche*. I tapped him on the shoulder, and even though he didn't want to let go of her, I insisted on my cutting-in privilege.

All the years of my adolescence I had been a poor suitor. Doubting myself, I was easily discouraged. Always I wanted the girl to make the advance. That evening I turned pursuer. I stalked Kiki, cutting in the moment somebody else took her away from me. I entreated her with all the clichés I could dredge up. *"Je t'adore!"* I whispered into her ear. *"Je suis toqué de toi!"*

It was amazing how easily I could say these platitudes in a foreign language.

"Ah, *mon petit lapin*," Kiki held her voice to a delicate hoarseness. "I can feel you."

"Come with me," I urged her.

"Where to?"

"It doesn't matter!"

It was midnight by then. The orchestra accelerated its beat, the drums deepened, the plumes, crowns, turbans, and wigs rocked in the dim light.

"Vieus coucher avec moi!"

She stared at me, her eyes brighter than ever. I waited for her answer, hardly daring to breathe.

"Eh bien—allons-y!" she said and led me determinedly out of the ballroom. "Here," she rummaged in her handbag, "get my coat!" She handed me her cloakroom ticket. "There are taxis outside. Get in

135

one and wait for me. I must make some excuses." Patting my cheek lightly, she rushed back into the ballroom.

The girl at the checkroom asked, "Why are you leaving so soon?" I just grinned foolishly, holding Kiki's coat. *"Ah ça—"* she smiled.

The night was cold, but I didn't put on my coat; I felt on fire. I stepped into the first taxi, told the driver to pull down the flag and wait. I held Kiki's coat close. It was redolent of l'Heure Bleue, which mingled in a peculiarly exciting way with the dankness of the taxi's interior. It was one of those venerable carriages that had helped win the Battle of the Marne. Minutes were ticking away in my heart. Suddenly the door opened and Kiki was at my side. I put the coat around her shoulders and gave the driver my address.

It was a short ride to the boul' Mich', but the driver pretended to be lost in the network of streets. Not that I minded. I had drawn Kiki close to me. Already we were like lovers. And like lovers we were silent.

At the boardinghouse, I was about to press the bell to rouse the concierge, when Kiki stayed my hand.

"Are you permitted to have visitors, *mon chou?*"

"Of course," I said manfully.

"At night?"

"No—not at night—" I confessed, and my courage left me.

Kiki smiled. "One should never put one's trust in a

136

concierge!" she said, with a gentle pressure of her fingers upon my wrist.

How true! Our Madame Vaché was the fat tyrant of 129 boul' Mich'. She lived in a single room behind a glass partition and clocked with mean, suspicious eyes the comings and goings of every lodger.

Returning late at night or in the early morning hours, I was required to call out my name as I passed the milk-glass window. Her acknowledgement was an abrasive grunt. I couldn't very well blame her for this, because I seemed to be the only tenant who aroused her from sleep at such late hours. Once in a while she would half-raise her massive frame from the couch situated behind the window, push the dirty curtain aside, and greet me with a glare of such poisonous reproach that I was stung with guilt and embarrassment. I had tried to sweeten her up by offering her money, but bribery did nothing to mellow her.

How could I get past that milk-glass partition tonight? I had a sickening vision of having to explain Kiki's presence to her.

Kiki, who had been living for years in all kinds of houses and all kinds of rooms, had the answer. I explained the exact location of my room, and she outlined her strategy: "You will press the button, and we shall both enter the house. But only you will pass by the old girl's window. I shall wait till it is all dark again, and then I shall come up to your room."

She slipped out of her high heels, and I pressed the doorbell.

A moment or two later the door opened automatically. The odor of stale dinners enveloped us. Kiki moved into the darkness behind the door, and I proceeded toward the glass partition. And that night the curtain was drawn. I faced the grim visage of Madame Vaché. I froze, struck by the enormous vulgarity of her face.

It was, however, the only note of ugliness, for there was no ugliness afterwards.

In the afternoon I had—maybe in subconscious anticipation—prepared the fireplace. Quickly I set the match to the coals. The fire drew well. I took Kiki's stolen image off the wall and pushed it into a drawer. I went to the connecting door and listened. All was still in Madame de la Porte's quarters. I straightened up and stood in silence. The only sound was the crackling of the coals in the fireplace.

Then the door was opened cautiously, and Kiki slipped into the room.

We walked toward each other. Her eyes seemed to light up the semi-darkness of the room. I found her lips. At the touch of her warm mouth, the smell of her skin, every trace of shyness melted away. Her tongue caressed my lips, then twisted and turned into my mouth. She guided my hand over her body. I closed my eyes.

"Why don't you take off your clothes?" Kiki whispered.

For one moment I felt a virginal shrinking.

She led me over to the bed.

"Go ahead," she said.

I took off my clothes.

Kiki watched me with a wonderful largesse and a smile so strong and encouraging that I felt warmth pouring all through me. Then she lifted the hem of her dress and, like a curtain going up in a theater, all of Kiki was revealed. She dropped the dress and stood for a while, letting me admire her. In the light of the fire her body was lovely: her legs white and firm, her breasts, erect and ample, seemed to welcome me. I felt like a wanderer enjoying the view after a long and arduous climb during which he has been given only a partial glimpse of the whole panorama.

I waited.

Kiki stepped closer. Turning back the covers and slipping between the bedclothes, she pulled me in beside her.

In the dark my hands reached for her. The warm pressure of her tongue was on my lips again—and then it began to explore me, moving slowly, knowingly, down the length of my body.

"Wait—" she murmured. "Not yet—"

She took hold of me with her hand, stroking gently, and then stretched out beside me. She still held me as she implanted me carefully into her body. I had the mystical feeling that she was initiating me into some sublime and religious rite. With her body, she gave herself totally to this single thing ... moving me in a rhythm of mounting excitement until I reached an explosion of senses so complete, so prodigious, that I seemed to float, to fly, to die.

Afterwards, in the stillness, she murmured affectionate approval. I had a sensation of freedom, of rapture, of deliverance.

The next hours were beyond the most fanciful fantasies of my youth. The restraining walls of an internal dam had given way, and all the years of longing and frustration were wiped out. I seemed to learn all that there was to know about the pleasures of love, though learning might not be the best word. Kiki simply enjoyed herself, enjoyed pleasing me, enjoyed giving. I learned that night that a woman could be gracious in a voluntary act of love, that she could make a present of herself without asking for anything in return.

Eventually we fell into an exhausted sleep.

A knocking at the door awakened me. "Monsieur—wake up!"

I jumped out of bed, raced over to the door, and told Madame de la Porte that I would not be going to classes that morning. I listened to her retreating footsteps.

Kiki slept soundly. Lipstick stains were all over the

140

bedclothes. In the partial light of the early morning I studied her lovely face, so relaxed, so soft and pleasing, so passionless now. I returned to her side, and when she felt my body she stirred, sighed, and turned over, thereby pushing me to the edge of the bed. I clung to her, and she opened her eyes. There was no surprise at seeing me. As if I were her one and only lover, she drew me close. My nervousness had been replaced by a confidence I had never known— my whole life seemed to have undergone a transformation. When I seized her again, it was better than it had been at night, for my thirst increased proportionately as I loved her.

Eventually she said, "It must be noon."

"Who cares?" I murmured.

"I do." Kiki jumped up. "One should never make love on an empty stomach."

With naked grace she walked over to the wall mirror and opened her handbag.

"I adore you," I said.

"But not too much, if you please," she said carefully and carefully began to fix her face.

* * *

We left my room together.

It was a bright, sunny winter day. My body seemed weightless, anointed, victorious. In my heart there was a youthfulness, a confidence, a gratitude, a singing joy—the triumphant feeling of an artist of genius who had just entirely expressed himself.

Madame Vaché stood in front of the house, and I greeted her cheerfully. I could have walked over to her and kissed her cheek. With the magical sense of relief that had taken possession of me, I was swamped with a feeling of gratitude not only for my initiation into physical love but into the more general love for all things, all people.

With peace and love in my heart, I steered Kiki across the boulevard toward the Crémerie Ledieu. I wanted to show her off to Jules, making him a witness to my triumph.

Though it was already past lunchtime, Jules still hovered around, and the final grace note to the symphony was struck: he looked at me with admiration. We ordered everything on the menu.

Kiki ate with the appetite of a starved, healthy animal. We were the only customers left in the small room, and we feasted on cheese and bread and milk and fruit. Kiki asked for wine, and though the crémerie didn't serve alcohol, Jules produced a bottle of vin ordinaire. Kiki's eyes were bright, her color was high. When we came to the end of the bottle, the last drop drained, Kiki reached out for my hand and, holding it, stroking it, she asked:

"How old are you?"

"Nineteen."

"You've waited a long time."

"It was worth it to wait."

We looked at each other in a warm, new understanding.

"You're quite a man," she said. "It made me very happy, *la bagatelle*—"

"Did you know it would happen?" I asked.

"Oh, yes. I knew it. Somehow, sometime."

For a moment we were silent, and then Kiki, still holding my hand, said carefully,

"You will get yourself a little girl friend now?"

"Why should I?" I was baffled.

"Because it is not healthy for a young man of nineteen to have no love."

"I have you," I said.

"I was your friend for one night," Kiki said. "The night is over. We will be good friends, but you must not pursue me any more. You've learned your lesson well. Now you're on your own."

Why should it be all over? I was stunned. My mind raced frantically for an explanation. But before I could entreat her, she had supplied an answer: "You must understand, *mon chou,* that I need a place I can call my home. Where I can work and have a bed, and where I can keep house and cook for someone and clean for someone, and someday maybe I can have Mouchette there with me, too."

"But—but—*you* must have someone to love as well," I stammered.

She smiled and said matter-of-factly, "It is important, I grant you, but the main thing is to have a bed of your own. Without it, one is a stray cat."

And she took my hand and pressed her lips to my palm, and I was greatly moved by the gentleness of that kiss. And I was grateful that by exposing herself she gave me a deeper look into her true self.

Her smile grew wistful.

"We shall always meet again," she said—and she looked at me as if from a high window in her memory, as if what had happened the night before had happened long ago. "And I shall always remember you with a happy heart. And you will learn that there is more than one donkey at the fair."

I still couldn't believe that it was all over, that I wouldn't hold her in my arms any more, that I would never again experience that sensual bliss. The thought of returning to all those empty evenings was like a specter of gloom ahead of me.

She must have guessed my thoughts. She withdrew her hand and laughed: "You're too serious, *mon petit,*" she said. "You must learn to laugh. Try!"

I tried, but it was a dismal failure.

Maybe later, I thought sorrowfully, I will laugh at this when I remember it, but I didn't feel like laughing then.

We said goodbye to each other. I looked after her as she walked up the boulevard and disappeared in the crowd—and I had the distinct feeling that part of my own being had left me forever.

I DREADED going back to my room, and I walked the streets till evening, fighting an impotent rage. Why had I given up so quickly? Why hadn't I asked her to keep house for me, to cook for me, to bring along Mouchette? It would have meant moving to an apartment, and my yearly allowance would have dissipated in a couple of months—but at least I would have had the satisfaction of having shown some initiative, of having put up a fight for her!

My bed was still unmade. There were some smears of lipstick, a strand or two of her dark hair, the strong fragrance of her perfume. I lay down and granted myself the pleasure of evoking her arms, legs, breasts, lips. She materialized in a variety of disturbing images. Her body emerged from the pillows. I felt the softness of her mouth, the caress of her hands, the roundness of her bosom.

It was a torment, but I was aware that it was different from my previous feelings of anguish.

I had possessed her. She had cured my growing pains. And while those yearnings had not lessened—

had, in a sense, increased—there was a change in my spirits.

There are more donkeys than one at the fair. The line kept turning in my head. A banality—yet I decided later that week to explore its possibilities.

I started to look around—hesitantly at first, then probingly—at other girls. I sensed the miraculous possibility in other women. Inside their different shapes and colors they might be as satisfying as Kiki. All I had to do was to reach out for them.

It was close to the beginning of spring then—and who, after all these years, can do justice to the beauty of spring in Paris? Butchers garnished pigs' ears with the first violets; the carousel in the Jardin de Luxembourg shed its drab winter cover; fountains began to play, casting their fine spray on the properly dressed children who sent freshly painted sailboats on gay voyages across the pond. A delicate blue hue spread over the city, and at the sign of it the first coffeehouse tables moved outdoors.

It was easy now to get up early in the morning and saunter down the boul' Mich', have a café au lait at the bar of the Brasserie Capoulade or the Café de la Source, and relish a hot croissant or brioche, just delivered from one of the bakeries on the boulevard. Bakeries opened at five in the morning and some kept their doors open all night.

While I stood and dunked my croissants, I watched the girls. Pretty or ugly, groomed or unkempt,

146

inspiring or ordinary—they all seemed dazzlingly desirable. It was up to me to choose from among them. My blood sang and I felt irresistible.

One morning as I entered the classroom of Professor Fauchet-Matignon, I became conscious of the familiar scent of l'Heure Bleue. I looked around and saw the strange girl again. She sat in the middle of the row where I had noticed her the first time, and again she listened in peculiar devotion to the lecturer. I moved down the row, close to her. She looked up, and I greeted her with a smile. Color rose in her face. She seemed to recognize me. But the next moment she returned all her attention to the professor's discourse on *la poesie romantique*. We had progressed to Baudelaire, and Professor Fauchet-Matignon was this morning in fine form:

Rappelez-vous l'objet que nous vîmes, mon âme
Ce beau matin d'été si doux:
Au détour d'un sentier une charogne infâme
Sur un lit semé de cailloux.

His recitation was inspired. When he had finished with a flourish, he looked up to the topmost row where we were sitting. She smiled at him, so obviously involved, so patently oblivious of everything else around her—including me. Still, it seemed to me that although she kept herself aloof, she was aware of my presence.

She wore a conservative but smartly cut blue ensemble, a handbag, white gloves; she was dressed for the city. I glanced at her legs. They were perfectly shaped, pink flesh shining through the silk mesh of the stockings.

Professor Fauchet-Matignon came to the end of his Baudelaire recital and switched to the usual commentary on the poet's style and philosophy.

The visitor rose, and, with an apologetic smile, tried to edge out of the row. I got up, but didn't move to the end of the aisle. In order to leave, she had to squeeze past me, and I did nothing to facilitate her exit. Instead of drawing back, I pressed myself against her. I felt her touching me. It was electrifying. My new boldness moved me to stare straight at her face. She smiled, a very sweet smile, but an impersonal and solitary one, directed rather to herself than to me.

She was young. Not older than twenty-five, I figured. I felt an urgent desire to know her, and as soon as the door of the classroom closed, I got up.

I rushed after her down the deserted corridor, following her womanly straight back, the trim hips, swaying slightly under the blue skirt, the long, perfect legs pushing through the slits in the sides of her skirt.

We were the only persons walking through the corridor. My footsteps reverberated along the stone walls, but she never turned her head to see who was following. She crossed the courtyard. A clouded sun was casting weak shadows around the two lilac trees. Now we reached the street. I was just a few feet behind her. Still she made a pretense of not noticing me. Purposefully she walked to the corner of the Rue Soufflot and the boul' Mich' and headed for the Café de la Source. There she sat at one of the outdoor tables.

I looked for a free table and there was none. I approached her boldly and asked whether I could join her.

She nodded formally.

It was accepted form to move a chair to a table occupied by a single customer and in no way considered a molestation.

"You're the most exciting girl I've ever laid eyes on," I said without engaging in preliminaries.

Her answer was a stunned look.

"I've thought of you ever since I saw you the first time," I went on.

This hypocrisy made me cringe inwardly. Its effect, however, was remarkable. Her face suffused with color and her eyes widened. Her reaction gave me the courage to continue.

"Why do you come so seldom to the lecture?"

"I live in the country," she said timidly.

"You're not a student?"

"Not any more."

She had a childlike voice with a slight lisp.

149

"You seem to like Professor Fauchet-Matignon," I went on. "And he seems to like you."

She smiled, the private smile again, directed at herself.

"May I guess?"

"Please do," she said.

"He's your father."

"No," she said and now the smile took on a quality of sadness. "He's not my father."

"A friend then?"

There was a pause.

She lowered her head.

"He's my husband," she said. "I'm Madame Fauchet-Matignon."

I stared at her in disbelief.

Her smile became self-conscious.

"I know—people are always surprised. There is quite a difference in our ages."

"Yes, there is," I said, and immediately felt it had been an idiotic thing to say. She was the wife of my professor, and the conversation began to make me uncomfortable. The compliment I had paid her suddenly seemed cheap. We sat wordless, at an impasse.

"Then I was correct that the Professor likes you," I said lamely. "He seems to recite the poetry to you exclusively."

"I guess that's so."

150

"He's a wonderful teacher."

"I don't know much about that," she replied. "I know that when he recites poetry he almost turns into a poet. In fact—" she hesitated shyly— "if it weren't for poetry, we probably never would have been married."

How unusual to tell me this! We hardly knew each other, and it sounded like an apology. Why did she have to offer me an explanation about being the wife of an old man? With a clumsy wit, born of embarrassment, I said:

"Did he woo you with verses? Like Cyrano?"

"The comparison is not far off the mark," she said and then her face and manner changed abruptly. Suddenly she opened her handbag and began a nervous searching through it. She said, "You must leave right away. My sister-in-law is meeting me. I see her walking up the boulevard. She mustn't see me talking to anyone. Please!"

I rose quicky, moved by the urgency of her plea. As I reached for my notebooks I had enough presence of mind to ask, "When will I see you again?"

"Next week," she whispered. "Same time. Here."

I went to the interior of the Source and ordered a drink. Above the bar hung a mirror at an angle which afforded a view of the terrace and the boulevard. I saw a woman approach Madame Fauchet-Matignon's table, shake hands with her, and sit down. The woman was small, with a good figure. She looked proper, plain, and undistinguished, and with her spectacles perched at that angle, she was without doubt the sister of Professor Fauchet-Matignon.

* * *

"She's even more jealous than my husband," Madame Fauchet-Matignon told me the following week. "She hates me in the same proportion as he loves me," she said artlessly.

It was a week since we had parted at the Café de la Source, and we strolled now along one of the side alleys of the Jardin du Luxembourg. Spring had come overnight. The first foliage had appeared on the trees flanking the alley, and the sky was brilliantly clear. Never had Paris looked so entrancing in the soft morning air. Madame Fauchet-Matignon wore the same blue suit, with the same gloves, the same handbag.

"Why should anyone hate you?" I asked.

"She didn't want him to marry me. They lived all their lives together. She never got married. Now she has to live alone, and of course she resents this."

"And how long have you known the Professor?"

The smile she gave me trembled. It was a smile unsure of itself, pleading to be understood: "Only a very short time. I was brought up in the convent, and when I left to stay with my aunt, Maurice—my husband—lived with his sister next door. He came over evenings, and we sat in the garden and it was summer and he recited poetry. I am a romantic girl. No one had ever read poetry to me. When he read poetry, he became the poet. To me he was Rimbaud, Baudelaire, Verlaine. When he proposed at the end of the summer, I was completely taken by surprise. I couldn't understand why such a man should ask me to become his wife." She paused and looked at me. Her eyes were fine and quite beautiful, not radiating the joie de vivre of Kiki's, but shadowy and mysterious. "You wonder why I'm telling you all this?"

"I'm glad you are," I said.

"You're a foreigner?"

"I'm not French, if that's what you mean."

"What country do you come from? What is your native language?" she asked guardedly.

I told her where I came from and what my mother tongue was.

She relaxed. It was almost like a sigh of relief: "I'm so glad you're not a German," she said. "For a moment I thought you were. In that case I couldn't have talked to you any more."

There were at the time quite a number of French people whose resentment against anything German was still in a ferment. The war had been over for years, yet the wounds were still open. Her father, she told me, had been a captain in the army and had been killed in the war. Her mother was alive—"If you can call living in an institution and suffering from melancholia being alive. All that," she said with passion and vengefulness, "is the doing of the Germans."

We found an empty bench near the Medicis Fountain and sat down.

"Shouldn't you be at school?" she asked.

"I don't go to *school* any more," I said, a bit stiffly. "I go to the Sorbonne. I come and go any time I feel like it. That's the difference between school and University."

"I shouldn't be here with you," she said in a low, guilty voice. "I should be doing my errands."

"You have the whole day for that."

"You're wrong," she said. "I'll meet my husband for lunch. Then we drive home together."

"How often do you come to town?"

"About once a week."

"And the rest of the week?"

"I'm at home. In the country."

She spoke matter-of-factly, almost like an unpleasant recital.

"How long have you been married?"

"One year," she said. It sounded like a weight falling.

"Funny," I said.

"Funny?"

"That you should be married at all."

"And to an old man, is that what you think is funny?"

It was all there in her voice now—anger and frustration.

"It's not what I meant," I said lamely.

"But *I* mean it," she burst out. "I didn't marry because I was so impressed. I was out of convent and I had no friends and I listened to my aunt telling me how fortunate I was that an elderly man should want me, a distinguished man, well settled, a pension waiting for him and a big house and a garden. A professor of the Sorbonne! And then—" she laughed ruefully, "—I did let myself finally be swayed by the music of his poetry. I was so young, so gullible."

I felt a divided sympathy. I was sympathetic because she seemed unhappy, and I was not so sympathetic because I felt in her confession the lack of a certain modesty and pride. Why would she tell a young man she had known only for a few hours a tragic mistake she had committed? But then, I rationalized, she was young. Maybe younger than I thought. And there was a need in her to communicate.

"May I ask how old you are?"

"Of course," she murmured. "I'm going to be twenty-two in May."

I was amazed that we were close to the same age. It occurred to me that the professor must have been her

155

first man. She had left the convent, and that summer they had met. And then they married.

"And you," she said. "What is your age?"

I told her. For a little while both of us were curiously pensive.

Then she turned her face fully to me, and once more there was the suspicion of a plea in her voice. "Is it really true you thought of me since you saw me the first time?"

For a moment I heard an inner voice of caution. True enough that I had thought of her from time to time, but in telling it, I had, of course, embroidered my feelings. Now she wanted to pin me down. But wasn't that what I wanted? To be pinned down?

"It is true," I said, and reached for her hand.

Her response was instant and frightening.

Oblivious to our surroundings, she threw her arms around my neck. Swept up by this outburst, I searched for her lips and kissed her. She responded with passion; there was an urgent, inarticulate quality about this kiss. She groaned and bit my lips, and I felt her trembling. It was a famished kiss, and it roused me—differently from the way Kiki's embrace had roused me, but the excitement was there, and the danger of being seen in the bright light of the spring morning only increased the excitement. Her eyes glistened and her face was flushed. She made no

156

attempt to conceal her agitation. We looked at each other, not quite believing what had happened.

"Je t'aime," she whispered—and collapsed awkwardly against me, breathing heavily.

The suddenness of my conquest overwhelmed me. We didn't even know each other's names. I asked her.

"Yvonne," she said.

I told her my name.

Then there was again a pause.

"Suppose someone had seen us?" I said foolishly.

"I don't give a damn!" she said fiercely.

This was strong language for a girl only a year away from a convent. I sensed that I would have to cope with the emotions that went with it.

And for a moment I wondered whether this was really what I wanted.

WE MET again—at the Fontaine de Medicis.

She looked radiant. "I didn't sleep a wink last night," she said ecstatically, pressing herself against me.

"I'm sorry," I said.

"Don't say it," she cried. "It's because I'm in love that I didn't sleep. I've never been in love." Her eyes turned moist. "I stayed up all night and I thought of you."

Of course it flattered me that a married woman should be in love with me, but the pace of the development, the unrestrained display of affection bewildered me. My situation had reversed itself. I had been the pursuer of Kiki. Now I found myself pursued by Yvonne.

"We ought to be careful," I mumbled stupidly, easing away from her embrace.

"We are alone," she said, looking around. "I don't love him. I never did."

"This is not the impression I received—" I hedged. "I watched you listening to him during the lecture."

"I'm very susceptible," she said. "I told you he has

158

a way of seducing me with noble words. He makes the poets sound as if their words were his."

"He's very intelligent—" I countered.

"Of course he's intelligent." Her eyes narrowed. "But his intelligence is a poor substitute."

"He seems a gentle man—" Ridiculously I found myself in the role of the devil's advocate.

"Yes, he's gentle," she cried. "He's gentle and intelligent and self-sacrificing, but there are certain things only a wife knows, and they can't be explained."

"Why can't they be explained?

"Because they would sound ugly."

"Why?"

"My God," she cried. "Are you really that naive? Don't you know that what counts most between a husband and a wife is what happens in bed? I can't go to bed with him. I can't touch him. He disgusts me."

The expression on her face had turned unpleasant. It was the same kind of unpleasantness I had seen when she had revealed her hate for all that was German. Seeing this change to uncontrolled loathing disturbed me. I looked away for a moment.

"But if you feel about your husband this way, why do you stay married? Why don't you ask him for a divorce?" I asked.

She hesitated. "I wouldn't want that, because—in a way—I am attracted to him."

"Attracted?" I felt lost. "But how can someone attract you and disgust you at the same time?"

Leaning slightly toward and gazing straight at me she said evenly, "You see I was terribly fond of my father. When the Germans killed him I thought I couldn't go on living. And when I met Maurice—well, he was a little like my father. Not in his physical aspects—my father was a terribly good-looking man—but otherwise. He was good to me, and I could ask him about everything I wanted to know and, like my father, he knew about all sorts of things and never tired of explaining them. And, like my father, he told me that he loved me." She smiled her private smile. "A girl never minds a man telling her that he loves her."

"And yet he is repulsive to you in bed."

"Yes."

"But how does he react when you refuse to make love with him?"

"I cannot always refuse him," she said with resignation. "Once in a while I submit, just to please him."

I wondered again whether she had had any other man before she married Professor Fauchet-Matignon—and I asked her.

She was silent, as if surprised by my question.

"No, I never had any man before my marriage," she said simply.

It suddenly occurred to me that her passionate confession of love for me had nothing to do with love. It was a plea to redeem an unhappy marriage with an aging husband. Her frustration had built up such a

160

pressure in her that the slightest flick would spark latent fire. And I was at least forty years younger than Professor Fauchet-Matignon.

It was that simple.

Yet, while her readiness was extremely tempting, I couldn't shake a feeling of fear. She was a married woman, the wife of my professor. Sleeping with a girl was one thing, but committing adultery was bound to bring ugly complications.

And then there was an uneasy doubt: Yvonne seemed to expect in me a prodigious lover. Would I be able to supply what her husband had failed to give her? And did I really desire her? Wasn't I more flattered by the fact that she wanted me? For an instant I felt panicky.

She must have sensed it. She gripped my arm hard and dug her fingernails passionately into my flesh. "Take me somewhere we can be alone."

"Where to?" My mouth was dry.

"Anywhere."

* * *

Anywhere was a hotel I had seen many times on my way to the Sorbonne. It was in the Rue Gay Lussac; the sign read: *"Hotel de l' Esperance, tout confort."*

There were a number of small hotels in our quarter where one could rent a room for an hour, a day, or a night, no questions asked. You didn't have to show any identification or register a name. You

161

just paid in advance and got a room key from the clerk.

The room we were given was gloomy and airless. It contained a narrow brass bed, a threadbare carpet, an age-colored plush chair, and a tattered screen that concealed the inevitable bidet. The odor of thousands of previous occupants seemed to have impregnated the walls of this chamber of horrors.

I felt like bolting. The vision of things to come seemed rather dismal.

We stood for a while motionless in the middle of the room. Then simultaneously we moved—in opposite directions. Yvonne walked over to the single window which looked out at a gray wall, and I went back to the door, about to run. The room suddenly went dark, and when I turned around I saw that Yvonne had closed the wooden French shutters. The darkness somehow brought a measure of courage. And so instead of opening the door, I turned the key in the lock—sealing my fate.

I still hesitated for a moment—but now there was only one direction to go. I saw the outlines of her figure in the semi-darkness, but we would have found each other in complete blackness anyway. Now she touched me, pulled me close, and searched for my mouth. She clung to me, pressing her mouth to mine.

Our bodies seemed to burrow into each other. She moved her mouth toward my ear, and in an inarticu-

162

late exhalation of words, she murmured, *"Mon amour, mon cheri, mon coeur, mon soleil, mon bebé—"* She drew my head down to her breast. My hand reached under her blouse. Her body had a wonderful odor, different from Kiki's, the fresh smell of sweet milk.

There was no longer any thought of failure. My hand searched for the warm well of her body. She moaned—and writhed.

Suddenly she pulled herself free. She tore off jacket, blouse, skirt. Then with the full weight of her body, she pulled me to the floor. I thrust myself into her. I responded to her ardor, to the outpouring of her repressed passion. Her hips rose and fell with a wildness all of their own. Her fury became mine, her body mine, until a loud outcry from her drove us against each other in a final, violent spasm.

We drew apart on the dirty rug. Suddenly, somewhat frighteningly, Yvonne burst into great sobs, as if she were drowning in some hopeless grief.

I stroked her head gently.

"What is it?" I asked anxiously. "Did I hurt you?"

"Hurt me?" she sobbed frantically. "I'm so happy, you'll never know. You made me happy, so happy." She began covering me with kisses—my face, my chest, my hands, every part of me—kisses of such devotion that I was greatly moved and responded in a manner which must have conveyed to her that I, too,

163

thanked her for the fulfillment we had achieved.

At that moment, I truthfully could have said that I loved her, but later I was glad I hadn't.

For it was far from the truth.

The real substance of the affair, to me, was the tryout of my new skill and knowledge—my gift from Kiki.

I CAN only blame my naivete and a very common form of male vanity for the continuation of a relationship which should have ended that morning in the hotel with *tout confort*.

However, I persuaded myself that Yvonne was, after all, a most attractive girl; that, in a way, I desired her; that she was a most alluring object for my awakened senses; that a liaison with her was very convenient and would not seriously change my life or interfere with my work.

Madame Vaché looked after an invalid tenant in our house between eight and ten in the mornings and was therefore not able to watch the coming and going of strangers during those hours. I had no difficulty persuading Yvonne to visit me in the mornings.

A few days after we met, she wheedled her husband into buying her a sports car. Up to then she had accompanied Maurice once a week to the Sorbonne and his daily lectures—using public transportation. Now she drove him to town daily, stayed a while at the eight o'clock class, then left on the pretext of doing errands or visiting friends—and slipped into

165

my room after knocking at the door three times as prearranged.

That we could make love in my room and not in the sordid surroundings of the Hotel de l'Esperance gave our affair a spurious dignity. That she committed adultery and that I was her accomplice ceased to bother my conscience.

I could have set the clock by Yvonne's knocking at the door. It was exactly eight-thirty, confirmed by the sound of bells from the nearby Eglise St. Geneviève. She was always in my room for the same length of time, and we always spent it the same way.

I would still be in bed when Yvonne would knock, enter, lock the door, and rush over to me. Her kisses were eager and abundant; soon she would undress and join me. She seemed to enjoy the morning sun that filtered through the slats of the Venetian shutters. The partial light revealed her exciting figure. From the waist up she was a slim and delicate young girl, but her hips and legs had a voluptuous fullness, muscular, solid, and strong. Our experience at the Hotel de l'Esperance had given me no opportunity to dwell on the sheer physical beauty of her body. But now each morning as she approached the bed—nude, covering her little pointed breasts, shivering slightly—I felt a steadily mounting excitement at the mere prospect of having her stretch out beside me.

Although her embraces were heated, there was an underlying timidity which was more expressive than

166

words. Am I good for you, her body seemed to ask, are you satisfied with me, will you keep me with you, will you not abandon me? To her I was the competent, seasoned lover, and because she thought of me this way, I became what she wanted me to be. We made love totally, shamelessly, without restraint. Afterwards she would lie spent beneath me, limp, smiling a lovely, satiated smile—and that was the best moment of our love-making. It was a very convenient and fixed idyll, a simple sequence of pleasure; if I ever loved her, it was in those mornings at the beginning of our brief union.

We seldom spoke. Partly because there was little intellectual rapport, partly because I didn't want to get involved in her private life and didn't want to encourage the kind of intimacy which carried danger of developing into love.

But it wasn't easy, because Yvonne was in love with me. She was possessive. She was jealous.

On one of her first visits, she discovered the portrait of nude Kiki on the wall.

"Who is she?"

"A girl I know."

"Did you know her—*this* way?"

"Yes—this way."

Pause.

"Did you love her?"

"Yes."

"Very much?"

"Yes, very much."

"Why?" She looked at me with troubled appeal.

"You love someone. How can you explain it?'

"Was she good at making love?"

"Yes. Very good."

"Better than I?"

"Different."

"In what way different?'

I considered it.

"Well—I guess *every* woman is different in making love."

"Have you had many girls?"

"A few," I lied.

"I thought so," she said—and smiled her private smile. "That's why I think you are good for me."

She cuddled up.

"Am I good for you?"

"Very good," I said truthfully.

Then, with some apprehension, "Do you still see her?"

"No. Not any more."

"The truth?"

"Yes. How could I possibly have another girl now that I have you?"

It was a sop to her self-esteem. I could have slept with other girls, too, for my virility seemed to know no limits. I never seemed to tire. There were mornings when, just as Yvonne was ready to leave, I would jump out of bed and have her again, fully dressed.

168

After she had gone, I would sleep till noon. Then I would get up, dress, and, over a huge breakfast at the Crémerie Ledieu, indulge in salacious exchanges with my friend Jules. Then I would walk to the Sorbonne to attend lectures or study at the library.

One evening I dropped in at my old haunt, the Jockey.

It was April now and it rained a great deal; spring, which had given false promise in March, was in full retreat. People in the Jockey were cold and huddled in their raincoats, since neither coffeehouses nor bars felt it necessary to supply heat once the first day of spring had arrived.

Otherwise nothing had changed. Everything was the way it had always been: the same posters, the same songs, the same faces.

I made certain that Kiki wasn't around, and then I walked over to the bar.

"Well!" Gitche Manitou said.

He lifted over the counter the bar stool he always held in reserve for a special customer.

"What will you drink?"

I ordered a beer.

He poured a demi-blonde and looked at me with calm detachment.

"You been sick?"

"No— why?"

I didn't think I looked sick, though I knew I might look drained.

"I've been working hard," I told him. "Exams." I avoided his eyes. I felt I had neglected him and needed to justify my absence.

"Sure," he said, twisting a piece of lemon peel into a drink. "You're a student. You've got to work."

He didn't believe a word I said.

"You haven't missed much," he went on, swabbing the surface of the bar. He eyed the room with loathing.

"How's Kiki?" I asked.

"Fine—I hope."

"She'll be here later?"

"I don't think so."

"Why?'

"She isn't singing any more."

"Really!" I was astonished. "What happened?"

"She lives with the *coqueluche*."

"But why wouldn't she sing any more?"

"She's kept busy," Gitche Manitou said flatly. Suddenly his hand reached across the bar and gripped my arm: "Have you seen her?"

"No," I said truthfully. It was about three weeks since she had been at my place, and I had decided to keep my mouth shut about it. Had I related my experience to the Indian, it would have hurt him, I was sure. He seemed to be relieved that I hadn't seen her; color returned to his face.

"One day she came for Mouchette and told me

170

about the *coqueluche*. He said she could keep her cat there. And then she asked me whether I would team up with her.''

''Team up with her?''

''She thinks she doesn't need the Jockey any more. Wants to run her own bar. Wants to call it 'Chez Kiki.' ''

''But you need money for that sort of thing, don't you?''

''The South American is well-heeled. He'll probably put up the dough.''

''And how about you?''

''How about what?''

''Will you—team up?''

He gave me a scornful look.

''Like hell I will,'' he said vehemently. I was startled at this unusual profanity.

I didn't reply, but he sensed my skepticism: ''You really think I'll quit here and go with her?'

''I think you will.''

I was sorry I'd said it. It disconcerted him, and he began to clean some glassware that was already sparkling.

A new girl, Poucette, appeared on the dance floor. People howled at her song, even though, or because, the song was bawdy and tasteless. It was in every line as crude as the songs Kiki sang, but coming from Kiki it would have sounded piquant.

Gitche Manitou leaned over the bar and whispered confidentially, "They're trying to replace Kiki. Ever heard anything in such bad taste?"

She sang an encore, and then the dancing started.

Gitche Manitou shrugged. "She left town. Two weeks ago. He took her to the Côte d'Azur."

"How long will she be gone?"

"She ought to be back soon." He went over to the cupboard behind the bar and came back with a postcard that showed a hotel in Cannes. It was from Kiki. "I'm glad for her," he said. "I'm glad he took her. She's never been anywhere. Never seen the sea. Imagine!"

"Can I read the card?" I asked.

He handed it to me.

"*Grand Chef*," she had written, "*Il pleut comme vache qui pisse. Mais je m'en fiche et m'en contrefiche. On se débrouille formidablement. Tendresses.* Kiki."

I had to smile. Always Rabelaisian. For Kiki it didn't just rain. It rained like a pissing cow. But her spirits were waterproof.

Scooping up the card, Gitche Manitou said, "Trouble is, she's given up painting. That character keeps her hopping like a roach in a skillet. Drags her to parties. Uses her as a come-on for getting commissions. I hear he's a fast mover, but I think he's bad medicine for her. Real bad medicine."

172

I understood his unhappiness about the new development, but I figured that Kiki must have been in love with the South American or she wouldn't have moved in with him.

"Don't you think she loves him?" I asked.

Gitche laughed derisively: "Rejoice, young man, in thy youth," and then, like a school teacher instructing a backward child: "Mouchette, yes. She loves Mouchette. And she'll love the Côte d'Azur and that hotel you saw on the card. She'll love that. And maybe she'll love the room she lives in and the big bed and what's happening in the bed. But I know she doesn't love that *coqueluche*. If only I were a believer," he concluded bitterly, "I'd believe one day she'll come back to me. But hope is the cruelest of all delusions. I am not good at self-deceiving, and unluckily, I am not a fool."

He muttered something short and obscene, and from then on ignored me.

Looking back, most of us can recall a moment in our life at which the pattern of our existence changed, when a word, a gesture, a look, diverted us irrevocably into a new direction.

One morning early in May, Yvonne lay on the bed next to me. It was hot in the room; the shutters were closed, and the sun hit the windows in full force.

"I wonder," Yvonne asked dreamily, "why you never mention my life with Maurice."

"Isn't the reason obvious?" I was disconcerted by her question.

"It is—and it isn't."

"Well, talking about your husband makes me feel guilty, and I don't want to feel guilty."

Yvonne sat up in bed.

"But you really don't have to feel guilty, *mon amour.*"

"Why not?"

"Because we have a much better understanding now, Maurice and I. And you brought it all about."

174

"I did?!" My voice cracked. My first thought was that she had told him about us.

"How could I have brought it about?" I asked her. She laughed.

"He's reaping the benefits of our affair."

"I don't understand."

"Well, first of all, he doesn't repel me any more the way he used to."

"Does this mean you go to bed with him now?"

"I went to bed with him before you and I met, but only if I had to. I told you—I just submitted."

"And now?"

"Now I let him have his way more often."

"Because you feel guilty?"

"No, because I am happy. Feeling the way I do, I enjoy making Maurice happy, too. I can tolerate him better since I know that the next morning I will be with you."

"And that's how he is reaping the benefits?"

"Of course. Everybody is happy now, don't you see?'

I saw.

And I didn't like what I saw.

The role of accomplice in revitalizing their marriage was one I didn't relish. I wished she hadn't told me. Suddenly everything took on a different shading: with the view that I was just performing a service for someone else, I felt an unwelcome sense of shame and slight outrage. And while Yvonne, who noticed that something was wrong, assured me that I was her one and only love, a cold stone settled in my vulnerable stomach.

I found reasons for cutting our daily meetings down to twice a week. I told her that I would flunk my exams in *la Poesie Romantique* if I didn't attend more of her husband's lectures. My attendance record had been poor as it was, and there were only eight weeks of the course left. Failing grades would make it difficult for me to return to school—and to her—in the fall.

Yvonne reluctantly agreed to the new arrangement.

So now there were only two mornings a week with Yvonne—but the excitement was gone, and I seemed to be unable to make love with the same ease, the same spontaneity as before. It had become an obligation, a routine. There was still that fundamental animal thing with a girl's naked body, but the flavor had gone stale.

Sensing that the distance between us had widened, Yvonne made a great effort to recapture our first enthusiasm, our inspired haste and eager complicity, as if trying to convince herself that my waning appetite was due to causes that had nothing to do with her person or her desirability.

176

One morning when I arrived to attend Professor Fauchet-Matignon's class, I was surprised to see her again at her accustomed place in the last row. I felt a shot of fear, an ominous foreboding, but she smiled at me, apparently happy to meet me in an extra-curricular way. She followed her husband's declamations with her usual rapture. After half an hour she rose, and wiggling past me, she slipped me a note. I was to meet her after class at the Café de la Source. She had one more free hour to spend with me. Three exclamation points.

I decided to meet her and also to tell her then that we could not go to my room. It would be at the time when Madame Vaché returned to her observation post, and I couldn't run the risk of being seen with a woman. It would be a welcome excuse.

At the Source, I looked among the outdoor tables for her but she was nowhere to be seen. I was momentarily relieved, but conscientiously glanced inside.

I spotted her immediately. She sat on one of the leather-upholstered benches against the wall and signaled me with a look of such desperation that I froze for a moment. She was not alone: Professor Fauchet-Matignon's sister sat next to her.

I responded instinctively by walking past them without any sign of recognition, ordered a coffee at the bar, and observed the two through the slanted

177

mirror above. Yvonne, her head bent, listening to her sister-in-law's chatter, was playing nervously with the spoon. The sister-in-law, considerably older than Yvonne, had the air of a governess. She was talking to Yvonne as if giving a child a stern lecture.

I watched them for a while, then paid. Just as I did so, the sister-in-law rose, kissed Yvonne perfunctorily on both cheeks, and strode out.

I allowed a few moments to pass before I walked over and joined her.

Yvonne's face looked both drained and excited.

"Imagine," she whispered, raising her head to make certain we were alone, "running into her here, of all places."

"You didn't have a date with her?"

"How could I? And telling you to meet me here! No, she suddenly walked in and I thought I'd die. A few minutes later and she would have caught us."

The remark irritated me.

"Caught us—drinking coffee!"

"*Seen* us."

"What would have been wrong about that?"

"I told you she is insanely jealous."

"About you?"

"About Maurice."

"You mean you're not allowed to talk to another man?"

"You're not just another man!"

"How would she know?"

"She'd smell it. You don't know Gilberte."

"Well, to hell with Gilberte," I said testily. "Come on, let's take a walk through the park."

"The park?" She looked alarmed.

"It's too late to go to my room," I told her curtly.

"Too late—why?"

"It just is."

"Well!" she exclaimed. "I don't want to go to the park. Sit at the table with me."

She searched in her handbag for a pack of cigarettes and lit one with a nervous clumsiness, as if smoking was a habit she had just picked up.

I sat down and told her, mostly to calm her, that we would meet next day as usual.

She took a few restless puffs and then turned suddenly on me: "Do you still love me?"

She was trembling.

I had never said that I loved her and I didn't want to be hypocritical now, but I was afraid of what honesty would lead to in her state. My answer was slow in coming: "Sure I love you."

She stubbed out the cigarette and her face twisted. She began to cry.

"Please," I begged her. "Don't cry. There's no *reason* to cry."

"I'm so scared you will stop loving me," she sobbed. "I couldn't face it."

She grabbed my hand and pressed it fiercely. Her nails were sharp. "You don't know what it means,"

179

she started—when a cool and precise voice cut in on us.

"Sorry to disturb you. But I must have forgotten my gloves."

We looked up. Gilberte had returned.

Yvonne's eyes widened with shock. She dropped my hand—too late, of course.

"A friend of yours?" Gilberte asked crisply.

For a moment Yvonne seemed paralyzed. Then she blurted out, "Yes, an old friend!"

Gilberte eyed us shrewdly, obviously speculating on the nature of our relationship.

I had already jumped up, waiting for Yvonne to make the introduction.

"Well, won't you introduce me to your *old* friend?" Gilberte said.

I spoke for Yvonne, giving my name and adding a few words of conventional politeness.

"You're not French," Gilberte said. It was not a question. It was a statement.

"No, I'm not," I said.

"German?"

"Ridiculous. Of course he's not German," Yvonne cried.

"He *sounds* like one," Gilberte countered.

I had never hit a woman and I didn't want to start then, though the urge was powerful. While I stood still, controlling my anger, Yvonne began looking around and under the table.

180

"If you're trying to find my gloves," Gilberte said, a bleak smile of satisfaction crossing her face, "you needn't bother. They're right here on the chair."

She picked up the gloves, turned on her heels, and walked out of the café.

"Oh God!" Yvonne moaned. "This is a catastrophe!"

"Why should it be a catastrophe?" I said, furious in my turn. "Why can't you have a cup of coffee with an old friend in broad daylight?" I was not so much angry at Yvonne as at myself. I should have foreseen the possibility of Gilberte's intrigue, since I had been forewarned of her jealousy and suspicion. I had been caught and I was chagrined at my carelessness, but, beyond that, my vanity was damaged because I had found myself tongue-tied and ineffective.

"Don't you see?" Yvonne said with a shaky voice, and again her tears began to flow. "She came back on purpose. She must have known about us meeting here . . . she was probably spying all the time!"

I told her it was absurd, but my voice didn't carry much conviction. Yvonne went on sobbing. I gave her my handkerchief, took her hands and stroked them, murmuring affectionate words. After a while she stopped crying and tried a little smile.

"The main thing is that you love me," she consoled herself. "You love me, don't you—whatever happens!"

It took a great effort but I said it: "Of course I love you."

I didn't think there was, under the circumstances, anything else I could have said.

* * *

It was of course a mistake.

Had I had enough courage to end our affair right then and there, none of the events that followed would have occurred—or at least not with such impact.

For the next two weeks I lived like a person who carries with him the suspicion that he has a dread disease but cannot make up his mind to see the doctor. I knew that one day I would have to face the unavoidable, but I sought to put it off as long as possible.

I permitted our relationship to continue, accepting Yvonne's assurance that her sister-in-law had obviously decided to keep peace in the family and had not reported our meeting at the Source to her husband. Yvonne appeared at my room twice a week as usual, and I deluded myself into believing that since the school term was drawing to a close, time would solve my problem without any effort on my part.

And after the two weeks, time did indeed solve my problem.

It was on a Monday morning, one of Yvonne's mornings. A knock at the door wakened me. I was still sleepy and glanced at my watch: It was only a little after seven—too early for Yvonne, I thought sleepily. Then the knock was repeated, and I realized that it came from the door connecting my room with the landlady's apartment.

I got slowly out of bed and crossed the room to the door.

"What is it?" I asked.

"Monsieur," Madame de la Porte said anxiously, "there is someone to see you."

I tried to shake my thoughts into reason. No one I knew would disturb my landlady at this early hour.

"Please open the door, Monsieur," Madame de la Porte said urgently. "I'm standing here in my night-gown." I took the step that separated me from the door, and opened it.

The shutters in Madame de la Porte's adjoining room were closed; in the half-light of morning I saw someone standing behind her.

"Come in!" I said.

I turned to open my blinds and caught a glimpse of my landlady's bewildered face, her mouth twisted, her nose casting her cheeks in shadow.

A man entered my room, and Madame de la Porte closed the door behind him. I turned from the nearby window and went into a state of shock at recognizing the visitor.

"Monsieur," said Professor Fauchet-Matignon, "I am not going to excuse my presence in your room at this early hour. My visit will be of short duration, because what I have to tell you I can sum up in a very few words."

He spoke like a character from a nineteenth century Sardou drawing room.

"I—I don't understand," I heard myself stammer. My hand groped for something to hold onto.

"You don't understand?" Professor Fauchet-Matignon came closer. He harpooned me with his eyes behind thick glasses; his face was even yellower than it had seemed in classroom light. "You don't understand because you are an ignorant foreigner. But not ignorant enough to have defiled the honor of a lady. You are now called upon to give an account of your miserable deeds. A man like you we call a *salaud*. If you were French, and of an age at which you could give satisfacton, I would not have degraded myself by coming here but would instead have sent my seconds to you. But you are nothing but a vile species of a foreigner—a common *salaud!*" He was breathing heavily, and he came so close that I felt his breath.

How wonderful it would have been to faint, to find time in the darkness to organize my thoughts. All kinds of frantic questions raced through my head: what did he know? how much? had Gilberte informed on us? And what could she have told him except that I was a friend of Yvonne's? A friend could mean many things. But could Yvonne have confessed?

"Won't you sit down, Monsieur?" I said thickly, weakly offering him a chair, just to gain time.

"I have not come here to sit down and exchange amenities with you," the Professor said with haughty anger. "I have looked through your files at the University. I have a complete dossier on you. I was informed that you have had clandestine and illicit meetings with Madame Fauchet-Matignon, my wife. I have come here to tell you that unless you give me your solemn word of honor—if there is such a thing as honor in your bones—to cease seeing Madame from this moment on, I will take immediate steps to have you expelled from the Sorbonne on grounds of behavior unfitting a student who is only a guest of the Republic of France and the University of Paris!"

With bells of fright ringing in my head, I was only vaguely following the professor's ornate speech. But there was a line in his threat for me to cling to, the only line that seemed to offer an exit. He had been "informed" of our meetings—who but Gilberte could have informed him? And all Gilberte knew for certain, I assumed, was that I had met Yvonne at a café near the Sorbonne. Gilberte couldn't even have known for sure whether the meeting had been by chance or pre-arranged. It was clear to me that I had to lie, to deny everything. Lying had never been attractive to me, for it carried with it the sickly flavor of impotence, but to lie now—to save my skin and Yvonne's marriage—seemed an honorable deed, the decent, the gallant thing to do. It's like a dive into unknown waters, I thought. I will dive, no matter how deep the water below or how frightened I am.

"Monsieur le Professeur," I said and laced my voice

with what I hoped was impressive sincerity, "this is all a horrible mistake. There has never been anything illicit between me and your wife!"

"You deny the accusation?" Professor Fauchet-Matignon thrust his chin forward menacingly.

"I deny that there is anything illicit about the relationship!"

"Then you admit you know her!" he cried, as much in fear as in challenge.

"Of course I know Madame," I said, trying for dignity. "I met her at one of your lectures, and we had coffee together and a couple of pleasant talks. I cannot see anything illicit about that!"

"And about my wife's coming to visit you here in your room, you do not find this improper?"

His mouth quivered. He stared at me with an expression of such fierceness that for a perverse moment I was seized with a compulsive urge to confess, to tell the truth and accept the consequences. But I pursued a lie that sounded convincing—even to me:

"Your wife has never come to my room!" I said with firmness.

"Are you telling the truth?" Professor Fauchet-Matignon said. He was still fierce, but under the ferocity I felt that he wanted this to be the truth.

I was more than willing to accommodate him. "I

swear it," I said, looking directly through his thick lenses into his eyes.

There was a long, long moment of silence.

"I was told—" and a pleading note was now clearly evident, "—I was told by an irrefutable source that my wife was seen entering this house in the morning. I talked to the concierge and your landlady, and both ladies confirmed to me that you sometimes have a female visitor in the morning—at the time when I hold my lectures at the Sorbonne."

He waited. My God, I thought frantically, he knows everything—yet he wants to be convinced that he knows nothing. Could I maneuver it? The professor's mouth hung slightly open.

My eyes moved uncomfortably away from his demanding stare and, searching for security, stopped at Kiki's portrait on the wall. Suddenly, a line of La Rochefoucauld flashed through my mind. *Il arrive quelque fois des accidents dans la vie d'où il faut être un peu fou pour s'en bien tirer*: sometimes in life, situations occur where one must do something mad to escape. "Mad" was the operative word. I forced my eyes back to the professor's.

"I don't know the 'irrefutable source' that told you about Madame Fauchet-Matignon's coming to this house," I said. "I do have a female visitor some mornings, it is true. But it is certainly not your wife!"

187

He was far from convinced.

"Who then?"

"My girl friend."

"What girl friend?" He was unconvinced. "Who is she?"

"There!" I pointed to Kiki—splendid, beautifully solid in her nudity.

Wordlessly he walked over to the wall and gazed at the drawing. He removed his glasses and replaced them with a different pair of spectacles. Then he stood for a long time examining the work.

"A beautiful girl!" he murmured.

"Thank you."

"And she is the one who visits you every morning?"

"Not *every* morning. As often as she can arrange it."

There was a long pause. Then the Professor turned to me, and his face assumed again an expression of suspicion and misgiving: "I don't believe you."

"Why not?"

"I need proof!"

"Would you like to meet her ?" I didn't know what made me say it. I felt sorry I had spoken, but it was too late.

"Yes indeed I want to meet her," Professor Fauchet-Matignon replied quickly. "Very much I would like to meet her."

"Well—" my voice was shaky. "I shall try to arrange it."

188

"You will not try," the professor said with sudden loudness. "You will tell the young lady to meet me here. Tomorrow morning. At the same time as now!"

It seemed not just a threat but a command.

"Until tomorrow," he said, and, not waiting for my reply, started for the door.

"You can leave this way," I said, indicating the door that led directly to the stairway.

He crossed the room and paused there.

"*This* door has direct access to your room?"

I nodded.

He answered with a grim glance and marched out, slamming the door.

I was rooted where I stood, feeling the backwash of the panic I had pushed aside. Down on the boulevard, the goat-herd blew his pipes. It was the signal for the goat-milk customers in our house to rush down to the street and get their supply fresh from the udder.

I saw my face in the mirror on the wall above the wash basin. It was still my face. There was no sign of what I had just experienced. I don't know what I had expected to find, but I felt that something should be different.

And then I wondered how on earth to survive the next twenty-four hours.

J ust stayed in the room, still in my pajamas, until long after he had gone. I couldn't do it, I thought. Go to Kiki and explain the situation and ask her to front for me? Impossible. She had told me, to be sure, to find a girl friend—but this was my business and to make her a party to it might destroy any favorable image she had of me. So that was out. Definitely.

What then?

I thought of my father and the sacrifices he had made to let me come to Paris. I had abused his trust. There was now a frightening possibility that I would be kicked out of the University, a disgrace I was sure I could not survive.

I felt checkmated. It was the wrong moment to take stock of myself, but *how* could I have been so stupid? Everyone had been spying on me: my landlady, the concierge, Gilberte. Gilberte! How much did she know? The thought that she knew and had told everything was a real fear. However, the Professor's seeming willingness to accept my assurance spoke against it. Indeed the quickness with which he had welcomed my story seemed to be a clear indication that Yvonne had not confessed, that in all probability, she had stuck to the "old friend" version of the meeting at the Café de la Source.

There was hope.

I walked to the window. The day had begun: across the street, Jules swept the sidewalk in front of the Crémerie Ledieu. The sight of him made me feel less alone. I decided to confide in him: more practical in the ways of the world than I, he might help me find a way out.

I began dressing quickly, anxious to get to Jules. But then a knock at the door gave me a new jolt of the fright that had begun to ebb.

What now?

It was Yvonne—by way of a special delivery letter.

Nervously I slammed the door on the messenger and tore open the letter.

"Mon pauvre amour," she had written in an obviously hurried hand, "we've been betrayed! I don't know what Maurice will do, and I cannot leave the house, because he has me watched. Do not try to get in touch with me, I beseech you, and, above all, don't admit anything! I've sworn that there was nothing between us, that we only met at the Café. *Du courage!* We will be together again. *Je t'adore!* Yvonne."

I had guessed right. Well, there was something to be thankful for: my courage to lie. Small consolation, but it lifted my spirits.

I ran down the stairs and crossed the boulevard.

Jules was about to return to his kitchen chores when I caught up with him, and I had to talk fast and urgently in order to make him drop what he was supposed to be doing and take time off to listen to me.

We walked to the nearby Jardin de l'Observatoire and there, sitting on a bench, I gave him a thorough briefing on the situation. He listened with an air of importance, relishing the role of the trusted confidant.

"Have you spoken to anyone about this?" was his first question.

"No. How could I have? It just happened."

"Good," Jules said judiciously. "Listen carefully to what I will tell you. There is nothing to worry about."

Jules looked solemnly at me.

"You must go immediately to Kiki and tell her everything you have just told me."

Oh God, I thought, what a brainstorm! I didn't need him to suggest something so obvious and so impossible.

"Your very existence is at stake, my friend," Jules said gravely. "You have no time to squander. Be on your way!"

"First of all," I objected, "I don't even know whether Kiki is in Paris. The last I heard about her was that she was somewhere in the South. But even if

192

she were here, I'd rather be kicked out of the University than humiliate myself in front of her."

"Brave fellow!" Jules said mockingly. "A gentleman above reproach! But *merde* with all that, my friend. You have to humble yourself to save your neck. Besides, I've met your Kiki, and she looked to me like a woman who'd probably relish an intrigue like this. You have nothing to lose, since your affair with her is all over anyway. You must appeal to her for help, and you'd better do it fast."

I shook my head. I wouldn't do it fast; I wouldn't do it ever.

Jules shrugged. "Then you must accept the consequences."

"And that's all the advice you can give me?"

He leaned back against the bench and gazed skyward for a few moments, deep in thought. "Open your ears," he said, "and don't go into a faint at what you hear. Ready?"

"Sure."

"I'll take you this afternoon to the whorehouses in the Rue Odessa," Jules said with a look of cunning. "You'll pick a girl who resembles Kiki and hire her to impersonate Kiki tomorrow morning in your room. There are quite a few girls who look like Kiki—that old professor has only seen her picture and he wouldn't know the difference. You prompt the girl on how to act and what to say and—don't open your shutters. I swear he'll fall for it. And for the money you'll be paying the girl, you could bang her, too!"

He waited triumphantly for my approval. Sadly I shook my head. The whole thing was just too Boccaccian for my taste.

"Well, sorry *mon vieux,*" Jules said, a bit sourly. "I think I gave you some excellent advice. If you change your mind—I'll be around. You're in hot water, no doubt about that."

He returned to his duties, and I walked distractedly away in the other direction.

The Paris sky, heavily overcast, seemed to weigh down on me; it served to remind me of how this disgrace would affect my family. I really must spare them, whatever the means.

I walked slowly, my eyes on the pavement, my feet taking me in the direction of the street where Gitche Manitou lived. I went reluctantly, because I thought it would hurt him to hear about my affair with Kiki. But he seemed the last resort: if there *was* a solution he would have it. Better to hurt him than my family.

Having come to this decision, I strode more firmly along to his house.

Old men have their set patterns; I knew it was time for Gitche to be preparing his lunch, as he had been doing when I had visited him at this hour before.

There was no answer to my knock. When I tried the door, it opened. I went on into the room, which was dark; the shutters were closed.

I walked toward the bed in the corner.

He was lying there, tomb-still, and for one terrible moment I thought he might be dead. Then his eyes opened and he lifted his hand in a feeble gesture of greeting.

"Are you sick?" I asked apprehensively.

"I guess that's what you'd call it," he answered deprecatingly. "I'm flat on my back. Rheumatism, the doctor says. All I know is I can't move."

The light wasn't strong enough to see the expression on his face or the color of his skin.

"Open the shutters," he said. "What time is it?"

I told him it was almost noon, and I opened the shutters.

Gitche Manitou blinked at the light, and I saw what the illness had done to him. Under the covers his body seemed wasted and frail; his face was etched by suffering.

He smiled weakly up at me from the pillows.

"I'd never been sick a day in my life. Then it hit me like lightning. I came home one night after work and bang, I was frozen stiff. Couldn't make a move. I've been lying here ever since."

"But who takes care of you?" I felt contrite for the weeks of neglect, for the friendship I had selfishly allowed to fade.

"The concierge—Madame Roulet. She fixes me some meals. Ben drops over in the evenings before he goes to work. And then the girls, Marcelle, Chiffonette—and now, Kiki."

I caught my breath. "Kiki?"

"Yes, she's back from the Côte d'Azur. She was here yesterday and she'll be back today."

"When?"

"Soon. She said she'd be here around noon to clean up and make me a soufflé. She's a fine cook, did you know?"

"No, I didn't know," I said. Nor did I care, really. Most of all, right now, I wanted to express my concern for the Chief, wanted to prove helpful.

"I'm awfully sorry about your illness," I told him. "I had no idea, otherwise I would have come right away. I was so involved in work . . . "

However sincere I felt, my words sounded hollow and unconvincing. My own problem obviously took precedence in my thoughts. Gitche looked at me shrewdly: "What brings you here in the middle of the day? Are you in trouble?"

I said I just meant to look him up. No special reason, absolutely none. I couldn't burden him in his condition with my difficulties. Besides, Kiki would show up soon, and the knowledge that I would see her again gave my heart a swift bound.

I hung around for a while trying to make myself useful.

Eventually I heard her laughter as she came racing up the stairs. She threw open the door. Chiffonette was with her, hidden behind a huge paper bag.

Kiki seemed genuinely joyful to see me.

"*Ma petite grue!*" she exclaimed, and hugged me hard. Then she held me at arm's length for a moment. "How have you been? I'm so happy to see you—you know Chiffonette, don't you?" Turning to Chiffonette and pointing to me, she laughed. "He'll get to heaven without even a confession, won't he?"

Chiffonette and I knew one another, if only slightly; while we exchanged greetings, Kiki went over to the chief's bed and bussed him, and wasn't it a lovely day and how did he feel and had he slept like a good fellow and had he eaten the soup she had cooked for him the previous day and had he tried to wiggle his toes this morning and how about *la digestion?*

I felt a wonderful elation, an extraordinary happiness at being near her again. Hope and charity had entered the room.

Kiki unpacked the paper bag: there were eggs and cheese and paté and a casserole: "Here is a *poularde de Bresse* for you," she said to Gitche and took the chicken dish over to let him savor the aroma.

"I was promised a soufflé," Gitche Manitou said with mock petulance, but sniffed appreciatively at the casserole.

"I know I promised the soufflé," Kiki said, "But it will have to wait till tomorrow. I can only stay a few minutes today. Chiffonette will clean up for you and feed you and spoil you and *ça va ronfler, mon grand becoteur!*"

Ça va ronfler; everything was going to be all right.

Of course, it suddenly struck me, everything *would* be all right. Watching her move purposefully around the room—straightening things up, patting my cheeks as she skirted by, getting a bowl of hot water ready, sitting down on the bed to soap the Indian's face, shaving him with unexpected deftness, and all the while telling him the gossip of Montparnasse and laughing with such natural heartiness at something that had happened at the Dôme—I knew: *ça va ronfler.* The worst I had feared just somehow would not happen.

When Kiki had finished shaving Gitche Manitou, she patted his face with a hot towel and then handed him a mirror. "Doesn't he look fine?" she cried, asking for our approval. Chiffonette and I stepped closer to the bed and dutifully admired her handiwork.

"*Demain on rasera gratis,*" Kiki said, leaned down,

198

and kissed the clean-shaven cheeks of the old Indian. His face shone.

Kiki brushed her hair back and gathered up her things. "May I accompany you down?" I asked her quickly. She looked at me uncertainly: "Of course, *mon petit*," she said, "but I have no time. I must rush home."

The urgency in my voice must have reached her, for she studied me with an air of curiosity and waited at the door while I shook Gitche Manitou's hand.

"I'll see you soon again," I said hastily. "Maybe this evening."

"Anytime."

"I hope you won't feel lonely."

"I don't feel alone at all," he said indicating a stack of books on the night table. "One is not alone with one's thoughts and one's books."

He smiled at me—through me. He knew why I had come to visit him. It was an embarrassing exit.

Kiki and I walked silently down the stairs. When we stepped out into the street, she linked her arm through mine. "You do not look too well," she said. "*Tu fais trop de truc?*" She winked.

"I've had my troubles since I saw you last . . ."

"Well then, tell me about them," Kiki ordered. I was conscious of her smooth skin against the texture of my jacket. "What's gone wrong?"

She had given me a helpful opening to what I

wanted to say, yet I hesitated. I was reluctant to bare my soul in broad daylight on the street. "Never mind my trouble. Tell me something about your trip. How did you like the Côte d'Azur?"

Kiki glanced at me sideways as we strolled along.

"*Merde* with the Côte d'Azur," she said gruffly. "First tell me your trouble—then I will tell you mine."

We had reached the Boulevard Montparnasse. There was a small bar across the way.

"Come on, let's have a little drink," Kiki said, and propelled me inside.

"But I thought you had no time?" I protested.

"One always has time for *un vieux copain*," she replied, and we moved toward the back, where it was dark.

* * *

Two in the morning.

I was lying on my bed, fully dressed, eyes wide open, staring at the ceiling. The shutters were closed; slivers of moonlight peeked through the cracks. The only sound was the occasional swoosh of a car on the street below.

I felt miserable. Here I was, dissipating a whole night's sleep when I meant to be fresh in the morning; there was really no reason to be anxious, because

200

things had gone well, incredibly well, everything considered.

In the back of the small Montparnasse bar, I had told Kiki what had happened: how I had met Yvonne and she had become my mistress and the crisis which now faced me. While I told the story, my eyes stayed concentrated on the little table between us. Not daring to look into Kiki's face, I listened carefully to my own voice so as to strike the proper tone between urgency and contrition—contrition for having exploited her.

When I had finished, there were a few moments of silence. Then Kiki laughed. I looked across at her uncomprehendingly. She laughed even harder, but at the same time she took my hand and put it to her cheek.

"*Quelle salade!*" she cried. "My little boy has grown up in a big hurry!"

The way she said it allowed a certain pride to invade my embarrassment.

She smiled warmly.

"You can be certain we shall give the old *cocu* just what he is expecting."

I felt such a surge of gratitude and relief that I had to control the start of tears.

"You really will help me?"

"But of course!"

I wanted to fly. Everything was suddenly going to be so easy.

There was one difficulty. Kiki and her *coqueluche* ordinarily slept till noon, so she would have to find an excuse to leave home and be at my place by seven in the morning.

"Tu est dans le pastis, mon petit," she said when we parted. "But have no fear. Here—give me your address." She handed me her lipstick and a paper napkin, upon which I painted my address, and when we parted she kissed me with tenderness on both cheeks.

Now, alone in my darkened room, I was nagged by the remote chance that she would find herself unable to slip out in the morning.

The silence of my room deafened and oppressed me. Sleep seemed out of the question. I got quietly up and left the house.

A soft spring rain was falling. I had thought walking would ease my apprehension, but my imagination kept pace with my steps, and by the time I returned home at dawn, I was convinced that Kiki had lost the napkin with my address, or that her friend would forbid her to leave. Not that it mattered—my imagination now had Yvonne making a full confession of her infidelity. I was a fraud, a liar, an adulterer—and after my expulsion from the Sorbonne, I would jump to my deserved ruin from the uppermost plateau of the Eiffel Tower.

By this hour of the morning, the vegetable trains were rumbling down the boulevard. The rain had stopped, the fog had begun to lift, and the vitreous blue of the morning sky appeared above the house-tops.

I stretched out on the bed, determined to tighten the reins on myself and see things in their proper perspective.

When I woke, the sun was high above the horizon.

Apprehensively I checked my watch: it was fifteen minutes past the time Kiki had promised to be at my place. I rushed to the window and leaned out—to find the streets empty.

At one dizzy moment, a part of me was detached enough for an observation of the picture I made—standing at the window in a limp, still rain-damp suit, waiting for someone who would never arrive.

In the distance, the Eiffel Tower faced me like a giant exclamation point.

I would not wait till the Tower's elevators were opened for the day. I would commit my body to the spring-swollen waters of the Seine. But why make even that effort? I could leap right from the fourth floor of 129 Boulevard St. Michel and let the city of Paris take care of my splattered remains.

203

I glanced out the window to gauge the depth. And that was when I saw her.

She was running up the boulevard, slowing periodically to check the house numbers.

I felt my chest expand to twice its normal size. I rushed from the room and flew down the stairs, meeting her just as she came through the front door. I dragged her in and embraced her. I tried to convey in my embrace all the wild gratitude I felt. She had saved my life!

Out of breath, she told me that she had been unable to find a taxi around the Rue de l'Estrapade, where she lived with the South American, and had run all the way to keep the rendezvous. Without hesitation I paraded her past Madame Vaché's window, and we climbed the four flights to my room.

The first thing Kiki noticed was my unslept-in bed. "*La barbe!*" she cried. "You have not slept!" I confessed that I had had a sleepless night, but now it didn't matter. Now that she was here, nothing mattered.

With the eyes of a stage director she surveyed the scenery. "You'll never get to Heaven like this," she decided. Without consultation she crossed to the window, closed the shutters, and unbuttoned her dress.

The garment quickly dropped to the floor—as

usual, she wore nothing underneath. She pulled back the bedclothes and slipped between the sheets.

I stood there, wondering whether she had perhaps forgotten why she was here. "Kiki," I pleaded. "What are you—? I mean—the Professor—he'll be here any minute!"

"I hope so!" she cried. "I hope I was told the truth—*sans blague!*"

"Of course it's the truth—"

"Then get undressed! Quick!"

"But I can't receive my professor in bed!"

"And why not? At this time of the morning one is in bed. If you're modest, you can wear your pajamas."

I had no mind of my own; my head whirled. But through the dizziness I somehow trusted Kiki, so I undressed in a trance and got into pajamas. When I stretched out next to her, I trembled so violently the bedclothes quivered.

Kiki chuckled and drew me closer. *"Ne bouger pas,"* she admonished me.

This curtain lecture was not necessary. I couldn't have made move one. The starchy image of Professor Fauchet-Matignon was in the room with me, and it hardly made for sexual stimulation.

"What's the matter with you?" Kiki asked.

"I'm just a little jittery."

205

She took my hand.

"Calm down," she whispered.

The touch of her soft, warm flesh made me feel better—so much better that I had begun kissing her when I heard the sound of footsteps, a knock at the door.

I wanted to answer, but Kiki placed her hand on my mouth, signaling silence.

"Who is it?" she called out.

"Professor Fauchet-Matignon."

"Come in!"

She tried to prevent it, but I jumped out of bed and rushed to the door.

"Please, come in, *Monsieur le Professeur!*" I said formally. I think I even bowed. "And please excuse—" Helplessly I indicated my pajamas.

He gave me a dismissive glance and peered behind me into the dark room, trying to make out the figure in bed.

Then he said stiffly: "Will you please make some light, Monsieur?"

He stood in dignified silence while I half-opened the shutters, and the light fell upon Kiki as she sat up in bed, drawing the sheet to her neck.

Professor Fauchet-Matignon stepped closer.

"Permit me, Mademoiselle—" he said with a flourish "—to introduce myself. Maurice Eugène Fauchet-Matignon."

"*Enchantée!*" Kiki said, aping his Victorian dignity.

"I assume," the Professor went on, "that your friend has told you about the urgency of my visit this morning. It is, believe me, a painful call I am undertaking, and I trust you will not consider it an imposition to answer a few questions."

"It will depend on the questions."

He smiled thinly.

"How long have you known this young man?"

"Since last autumn."

"And—with your indulgence—you are sharing certain intimacies with him—since when?"

"With your indulgence—since quite some time."

"Every day?"

"Every day."

Pause.

"Now I will leave it to your discretion," he went on, "to tell me whether it is conceivable that your young friend is conducting other relationships of an amorous nature besides the one he is entertaining with you?"

Kiki gave him an exaggerated look of incredulity and then, as though he had said something immensely funny, she gave a shriek of laughter: "My dear sir, I don't believe it would be humanly possible for this young man to be having another amorous relationship, as you put it!"

207

There was no immediate reaction from the Professor, but somehow the atmosphere lightened considerably. Kiki's laughter had obviously been persuasive. The stiffness of the Professor's back relaxed. He moved his feet apart and assumed a certain casualness.

"I am very beholden to you for this forthright statement, Mademoiselle," he said guardedly.

He turned to me, addressing me now for the first time.

"I am glad for you, young man," he said urbanely. "Your little friend is most convincing—" he stopped as a new thought crossed his mind. "What is this lady's name? You have not introduced her to me."

"Forgive me!" I said hastily. "This is—Kiki."

"Just Kiki?"

"Just Kiki," Kiki said.

"Kiki is a painter," I said.

"How interesting," he said. "And what do you paint, Mademoiselle?"

"I can show you one of her drawings—" I hastened to my desk and brought it out.

Professor Fauchet-Matignon took it and walked over to the window to catch the proper light.

"Delightful!" he said.

"Kiki had an exhibit a few weeks ago," I said with vicarious pride. "All of her work was sold."

"I don't understand much of this sort of art," he

said, benevolently patronizing, "But it certainly does have a charm."

"Thank you, sir," Kiki smiled coquettishly. "I shall send you an invitation to my next show."

"I shall make use of it with pleasure, Mademoiselle," the professor said with a flourish.

There was really nothing more to discuss, and I expected him to leave.

Yet he hesitated. There was something more on his mind. Thoughtfully he sucked in his cheeks. Then he paced to the wall where Kiki's portrait hung and studied it at some length. His eyes traveled from the drawing back to Kiki. Her hands still gathered the sheet protectively over her bosom.

"Yes," he said at last. "It is you. I can see that. The same face—"

"My dear Professor," Kiki said quietly, "we don't want you to leave here with even the smallest doubt, do we?" With a smile of angelic sweetness she slowly dropped the sheet.

Professor Fauchet-Matignon stopped breathing. I don't think his glasses actually steamed up, but he removed them and put them back on again. A sound came from his throat which most likely was meant to be a laugh, but it was quickly choked off, as though he had abruptly become aware that what he was eyeing was nothing to be laughed at.

"*Merci, Mademoiselle,*" he murmured, "*merci.*"

He waved his hand as if indicating that she could replace the covering sheet.

"It was nothing," Kiki answered with a smile, not moving.

He was hardly insistent about the sheet: he took one last, long look at Kiki's marvelous bosom, bowed solemnly and moved toward the door. I rushed over to open it for him. He gazed at me with envious, almost mischievous eyes, said nothing, and left the room.

I looked at Kiki. She smiled. I felt giddy and weightless, as if after some long, wasting illness. And then, infected with Kiki's amusement, I began to smile. Our smiles turned to laughter. Laughter began rising in me, climbing upwards. With the heady swiftness of triumph I lunged at her. Again, and for the last time, she welcomed me in her arms, and we made love joyfully, and when we were spent our laughter continued. It was the laughter of good lovers and good friends, and Kiki hugged me and chuckled softly. *"Merde alors,"* she whispered in her hoarse, sensual voice. "You have learned your lesson well, *ma petite grue*. You must have had a teacher *par excellence!"*

A LL THIS happened long ago.

And I have written it down from memory which came in waves like the surf of the Pacific I can watch from my window.

There is much I have left out, much I wanted to put in but somehow forgot, for nothing is more imperfect and treacherous than memory. But what I remembered I have recorded, trying to separate the important from the unimportant, the sweet from the sordid, the pithy from the trivial, in the full knowledge that such evaluation is of little use because everything I remember is important, even though much of it might not have seemed so at the time.

I left the Sorbonne at the end of the school year without seeing either Yvonne or Kiki again. And though I meant to return in the fall, it was almost thirty years before I revisited Paris.

I kept up a desultory correspondence with Jules Ledieu. Having been my confidant in *l'affaire* Kiki, he made it his mission to report to me everything he culled from rumors and clippings concerning Montparnasse and my great love. From him I learned that she had indeed opened her own cabaret, "Chez Kiki," which became a transient success where the crowd danced to the hit tunes of the period: *"Pas sur la Bouche,"* and *"Je cherche après Titine."* She never gave up modeling. She had film offers and appeared in mediocre French movies which in turn prompted an American motion picture company to invite her for a test. She traveled to New York, but the test never came off. Kiki felt strange and unhappy in the New World and, refusing to learn English, she simply took the first boat back without facing the camera.

At the end of the Twenties she published her memoirs, *The Education of a French Model.* In these reminiscences she told of her youth in Burgundy, her adventures on Montparnasse, her experiences as a model.

Jules sent me the French newspaper in which the confessions appeared. I feared that, ironically, Yvonne and her husband still would be compromised after all these years. Worriedly I scanned the pages for the episode which involved a certain foreign student and his cuckolded professor. I recognized some of the stories she had told me but—everlasting gratitude to Kiki—she never mentioned my affair.

Eventually Jules's reports stopped. It was at the beginning of the Thirties, and twilight had enveloped Europe. The effects of the crash were felt all around the world. Economic and spiritual values changed.

"An era was over," Hemingway wrote. "It passed along with the kidneys of the workers who drank along with the bums on Montparnasse. The bums were fine people and proved to have stronger kidneys finally—for they rested during the day." He wasn't worried about Kiki's kidneys, he wrote, because "she comes from Burgundy, where they make these things better than they do in Illinois or Massachusetts."

He was too optimistic. Troubles came to Kiki in the Thirties, troubles that didn't leave with the morning, that didn't leave her until the end.

But I am running ahead of my story.

I hadn't planned it this way, but as events find their own place in life, it happened that more than a quarter of a century slipped by before I visited Paris again, during the gray period after World War II.

It is said that you can leave and go a long, long way and stay away a long, long time, that you can cross seas and mountains and discover new worlds, but that when you return to Paris, she will always be there waiting for you, familiar and unchanged.

I wish I could say that it was thus with me. But the Paris that I saw again in the dead of winter held no welcome for me. It was a place from which all joy had fled, a barren city. The ghosts of war still hobbled through its streets. Gloom and sorrow drifted in the air. Hotel rooms were insufficiently heated, restaurants served indifferent food, taxicabs were on strike. I had arrived with festive expectations. They were quickly dissipated.

Depressed, I descended into the chilly catacombs of the Metro and headed for Montparnasse, knowing that in this corner of the city, at least, the spirit of Paris would surely have survived.

The whole evening remains in my mind with a dreamlike improbability. There are times when I am convinced that it never happened, that I never returned to Montparnasse, that I am in one of those measureless caverns of imagination in which writers often take refuge.

The old landmarks of my youth were still standing—the Dôme, the Rotonde, the Select—but they were glum and lifeless. I walked through the almost deserted rooms of the cafés, searching for a face I could recognize from the past. There was a waiter at the Dôme whose features looked familiar, but when I addressed him, it turned out that he had just started to work there and, judging from the few customers, his working days were numbered.

I walked up the boulevard to the Jockey. No neon light greeted me—nothing but the melancholy sound of a lone piano. The doors were open and I went in.

It was the same place, all right—with a slightly changed decor. A waiter hovered around me, pleading with me to stay: the *divertissement* would start practically immediately. I stared at his blue hands, chilled by the cold which was not at all affected by the single infra-red fixture that extended from the ceiling. A scene of ghostly familiarity was taking shape. I caught sight of the piano player. It was Ben. He had aged like a woman—his hips and face had broadened. Seeing a customer, he smiled up at me with a flabby, commercial charm.

But I was incredibly happy to see him, the man who once had carried me in his arms to Gitche Manitou's room. I rushed over to shake hands with him. He looked surprised at the effusiveness of a stranger. I identified myself, reminded him of the hilarious time he had had when he helped me in my cups to bed. He smiled amiably and pretended to remember me.

My first question was about Gitche Manitou. What had happened to him? Was he still alive? Ben shrugged. Our Indian chief friend had returned to the United States before the start of the war and nothing had been heard of him since. Very possibly he was still alive.

And Kiki?

"Ah—Kiki!" Ben said and shook his head dolefuly. "Poor Kiki. A sad story."

"Is she here? In Paris?"

"Of course she is in Paris. Where else?"

"Is she still singing here?"

"Here?" Ben laughed softly. "No, my friend, this place is gone to seed, as you can judge for yourself."

He cast a contemptuous glance at the bar, from behind which a bald, elderly man watched us with a humble look. "He's the new owner. Hasn't paid me for a month. But I don't mind. I'll go on playing here till I fall off this chair. But if you want to see Kiki—she sometimes drops in at Adrian in the Rue La Brea. Even sings when the mood strikes her."

"Has she got a man?" I felt as if I were digging in a graveyard for more decay.

Another chuckle. "I don't think a man would want to have her these days. When you see her you'll understand." He began playing again but went on talking to me. "There are some characters in this world who are marked down for self-destruction, and to them no rational argument can appeal. For my part, Kiki was always one of them—even in her heyday."

"Was she here all the time—also during the war?"

"Not all the time. She worked for the underground, and one day the Nazis got wise to her. They almost caught her—" he lifted one hand from the piano in a throat-cutting gesture. "But someone tipped her off, and the Maquis smuggled her out of town just in time. She went into hiding in Burgundy and only came back after the war. If you remember Kiki, you know she wouldn't want to be anywhere but here in Montparnasse."

"But what is she doing? Is she painting?" I asked, knowing what the answer would be.

Ben's smile was gently mocking, yet compassionate.

216

"I don't think she could hold a brush any more. Something happened to her when Gitche Manitou left. Once he was gone, she started to drink. I mean, she was often in a state of the jimjams, you know, but then she started on the big spree and stayed with it. Well—" he ended the song with a rippling arpeggio— "I guess all of us indulge in a few small follies to make life bearable, but poor Kiki sure picked the big ones."

My talk with Ben ended, on a note of muted panic. I decided to return to the hotel on the right bank without trying to see her again. What foolish hopes I had been nourishing! Those youthful experiences, burnished by memory, had lain all these years like a sparkling treasure upon which I might one day draw. Now I found myself suddenly bankrupt.

And yet, when I left the Jockey, I began looking for the nightspot called Adrian. Why did my resolve to flee reverse itself? What did I expect? Why that eagerness to find the bar where I might see her once more? Was it to gain a new evaluation of an experience that had marked me for life? Was it to return to it once more in order to shed it forever?

Chez Adrian, in the Rue La Brea, was a place where, in spite of a sparkling bath of colored light and subdued music, the atmosphere was stale and flat. The few guests, neighborhood habitués, all seemed to know each other, and they generated a sort of communal shabbiness. It was a place to get drunk quickly, and I ordered a bottle of champagne. The waiter became embarrassingly obsequious when I ordered a vintage bottle. I inquired about Kiki. Ah—had I come to hear the famous Kiki? Yes, I said, that was my reason for coming here. Kiki would show up later, he said, not sounding too sure. Certainly? Well—*almost* certainly. Lately she had been appearing quite consistently—it was indeed worth waiting for that. Had I ever heard her sing?

Yes, I said, I had.

I waited. I was on my second bottle when the door to the bar opened. An icy draft passed through the room. I looked up and saw her come in. She wore a shabby sealskin coat and a ridiculously huge hat. A veil covered her eyes. The waiter made a point of coming to my table. "Here she is," he whispered. "Kiki of Montparnasse."

I was shaken. More than that. It was as if some terrible explosion had occurred, leaving behind nothing but ugly fragments.

I was frightened.

I studied her face as she staggered toward the bar, studied it with a sadness I don't remember having ever felt before.

Ceremoniously, the waiter helped Kiki out of her coat. Under it she wore a black dress with a deep decolleté. She had grown thick. But it wasn't her figure, which had always leaned toward fullness, that had undergone a savage change. It was the face. Kiki's

218

face was almost destroyed by age. It was a face that seemed close to death, a face out of which the corpse peered. The heavy pack of make-up only exaggerated the portrait of terrible dissolution.

She clung to the bar to steady herself — her legs seemed rubbery, unreliable. She nodded to the pianist and he started with a little flourish. The dozen or so guests in the bar applauded perfunctorily. Kiki affected an artificial smile and began to sing.

I closed my eyes. It was a song I remembered. Curiously enough, her voice had not lost its abrasive charm. Yet there was an emptiness in the familiar lines; it was a well-known song that had lost its meaning. Before she reached the end, her voice grew furry and moist, blurring the edges of the words.

Again a thin scattering of applause. The waiter leaned over the bar and whispered into her ear. She looked in my direction; she seemed to be deliberating. Then she pushed herself away from the bar and walked unsteadily over to my table.

I rose.

As she came closer, I could see the thick mascara around the eyes, the ghastly sheen of the make-up. She smiled at me.

"You came to hear me sing?" Her voice was harsh and rasping, her breath smelled of alcohol.

"*Américain, vous?*"

I nodded.

"Yes, I'm American," I said, recalling that those

words were the first she had once addressed me with. Then I had not been an American.

"*Je m'en fou de l'Amérique,*" she said, and the look on her face was not pleasant. Her eyes fastened on the champagne in the bucket.

"Can I invite myself?"

"Of course, please," I said and she flopped down on the seat beside me.

I signalled the waiter, who was already standing by with a fresh glass.

I poured her champagne and we toasted each other.

She studied my face.

"Do I know you?"

I hesitated for the briefest moment before I answered.

"No," I said.

"But the waiter told me you—"

"I mean—" I stammered, "I heard you at the Jockey—long ago."

"Oh—when was that?"

"In the Twenties."

"And this is the first time you're back in Paris?"

"Yes," I said.

She laughed a little, humorlessly. "And I know what you're thinking. What a *vieille putain*. How gay she was! And how horrible she is looking now. But it is just the winter. Come back in spring and you'll see the difference." Suddenly she lifted her hands in a childlike gesture, awkwardly imitating a bird flapping its wings. *"Sur le printemps de ma jeunesse folle, je resemblais l' hirondelle qui vole, puis ça, puis la . . ."* she sang. Then poured herself another glass.

"Salut!" she said indifferently.

"Salut!" I said.

She emptied the glass and got up. She struck a familiar pose. For a moment there was a faint echo of the old bravado, of invincible courage—then she stumbled. I caught her by the elbow and guided her back to the bar.

"Merci, Américain!" she said with a despairing smile on her face.

I listened to her second song.

A terrible emptiness invaded me. It had been like something in a bad movie—or in a bad life.

I applauded when the song was over, and paid and walked away without looking back.

* * *

She died a year later.

It was on a Sunday; she had gone to the country to spend the day with friends when she suddenly collapsed.

There was no money to pay for the funeral. Someone took up a collection in the Montparnasse cafés, and the donations were enough to buy a fine casket and flowers and a quiet drink afterwards for her *copains* at the Dôme. Later on an old painter friend went to the room where she had lived the last year, to collect her scant belongings.

221

At the door he found a note in her handwriting.
"Partie—Kiki."

She had gone away—but had she gone away forever?

She lives in my mind the way she was then, a girl of
seductive charm and gallant spirit. She lives on in her
touching drawings, and in hundreds of portraits and
photographs in an ever-changing variety of images—
the tender Kiki, the tough Kiki, the demure Kiki, the
lascivious Kiki, the adorable Kiki—but still and always Kiki of Montparnasse, who never had a room of
her own, but whose lilt and laughter will echo
through the streets of Paris forever.